MATERIALISM

MATERIALISM

BY

J. S. HALDANE, C.H., M.D., F.R.S.

Hon. LL.D. (Birmingham and Edinburgh)
Hon. D.Sc. (Cambridge, Leeds, and Witwatersrand)
Fellow of New College, Oxford, and Honorary Professor
Birmingham University

HODDER AND STOUGHTON

LIMITED   LONDON

Made and Printed in Great Britain.
Hazell, Watson & Viney, Ltd., London and Aylesbury.

PREFACE

THIS book is a collection of essays or addresses, all of which bear on the subject from which the book takes its title. Materialism may be defined as the belief that physico-chemical realism, or the assumption that the representation of our surrounding universe by the physical sciences in their traditional form corresponds to reality, can be extended so as to cover, not only the phenomena of life, but also those of conscious behaviour.

We have inherited from the times of Galileo, Descartes, and Newton the belief that the external universe can be interpreted, without residue, in terms of physical, including chemical, conceptions. But until more recent times the phenomena of life and of conscious behaviour were usually excluded from the scope of this interpretation, so that traditional physical science could not be called materialistic. Roughly speaking, it left us with the conception of a physical world and a spiritual world existing side by side with it. The artificiality of such a separation has become evident in recent times, however ; and the modern world, in so far as it holds to traditional physical science, is driven towards the materialistic attempt to interpret our whole universe in terms of physical and chemical conceptions.

Although antiquated as a philosophical system, materialism is still very much alive on the scientific and practical sides, and it is from these sides that I have approached the subject. Several well-known recent books have been concerned with the ultimate break-down of traditional physical conceptions in connection with what we distinguish, however artificially, as the inorganic world. With this particular aspect of the break-down the present book does not deal directly. What is dealt with is the impossibility of interpreting the phenomena of life and of conscious behaviour in terms of physical conceptions, and the final necessity of a spiritual interpretation of our universe.

The argument which runs through the book is that, although the physico-chemical interpretation of our experience has endless practical uses, it is only a partial or abstract interpretation, which shows its complete inadequacy when the attempt is made to apply it to the phenomena of life and conscious behaviour. What ultimately takes its place is a spiritual interpretation, with a spiritual universe far better understood than when a spiritual was taken to exist side by side with a physical universe, and consequently as something " supernatural."

The fact that the book is a collection of essays will, I hope, make it easier to read. On the other hand, a good deal of repetition was unavoidable with this plan. Where there is repetition, however, the same subject is approached from different angles.

The first and fourth essays have been published before in earlier form, but are now considerably revised. The seventh is reprinted unaltered, except for a slight change in the title, from the *Transactions of the Institution of Mining Engineers*.

OXFORD, *May* 1932.

CONTENTS

CONTENTS

I

THE INSTITUTES OF MEDICINE
AND SURGERY [1]

ALTHOUGH Medicine and Surgery, in all their
branches, are practical arts, based on the accumulated empirical experience of many centuries, they are also based on general principles
derived from observation of living men and
other organisms in health and disease, as well as
from observation of inorganic phenomena. It
is these general principles, and not any special
part of the vast body of empirical knowledge
which they serve to cement together, that I wish
to discuss in this lecture. Medical practice
embodies ethical principles also ; but they will
not be considered here.

In the Scottish universities physiology has
for long been also called institutes of medicine.
Physiologists still cling to this old title, though
they rightly claim that physiology is based on

[1] Based on an address to the Middlesex Hospital Medical
Society.

far more than what has been observed in the course of medical practice—so much more that it is now no longer possible for one teacher to combine an adequate knowledge of physiology with more than a very meagre knowledge of practical medicine and surgery.

Medicine and surgery make use of various other branches of knowledge besides physiology. We may instance physics and chemistry, and with them mathematics. Normal and pathological anatomy are further prominent instances. Why, then, should physiology claim to represent in any special sense the institutes of medicine ? On the surface the claim does not seem admissible. No one would say that physiology is not of the greatest use in medicine, but I think that many would object to admitting that medicine is in a special sense based on physiology, and could give very cogent reasons for their objection. In any case, there is no denying the fact that a knowledge of physiology as at present taught does not occupy in medicine and surgery the position which it would presumably occupy if it represented in any actual sense the institutes of medicine.

It is evident that the reason why in former

times physiology was regarded as the institutes of medicine was that physiology, like practical medicine, deals with the living body, while other subjects, such as normal and pathological anatomy or chemistry, were supposed to deal only with what is inanimate. The difference between animate and inanimate seemed so great that the other subjects appeared to be much farther away from medicine. In the latter half of last century, however, the mechanistic movement in physiology tended to place physiology as actually taught on a par with the physical sciences. Physiology came to be treated as simply the application of physics and chemistry to the phenomena of life. Side by side with this change in the attitude of physiology we can trace a growing estrangement between physiology and practical medicine, till at last it has come to seem to those in medical and surgical practice to-day that a great part of the physiology which they were taught and examined upon might well have been omitted from their course of instruction.

Let us now consider the reasons for this state of affairs. In practical medicine and surgery we have before us a departure from the normal activities of life, together with, usually, an evident departure in some respect from normal bodily structure. But we also have constantly before us the fact that disease or injury is usually recovered from, either completely or partially, and that medical and surgical aid can aid enormously in arresting disease and promoting recovery. It is naturally the therapeutic side of medicine and surgery that interests us most ; but in connection with therapeutics and the processes of recovery current physiology has very little to say, though it has much to say in connection with the interpretation of symptoms. Quite evidently, the failure of physiology to furnish theoretical guidance in connection with the recovery from disease and injury is the reason why physiology is no longer looked upon as the institutes of medicine.

If we go farther back and ask for the reason of this failure, the answer is equally clear. Current physiology teaches that life is nothing but physical and chemical mechanism ; also that this mechanism must, in view of the extraordinary delicacy and precision of physiological reactions, be extremely definite and complicated. When any piece of mechanism is deranged it does not recover, but goes from bad to worse unless it is repaired. We can repair a steam-engine or a watch ; but the assumed machinery of the body is so extremely delicate that we cannot even come in sight of repairing or restoring it by any direct means. Yet as a matter of fact we are constantly witnessing the functional restoration of the supposed machinery, and the efficacy of medical and surgical interference in aiding the restoration. The physiology that throws no light on this can lay no claim to be the institutes of medicine. One searches in vain, from beginning to end of a representative modern textbook of physiology, for the missing light.

The older vitalistic physiology of former times had at least something to say about the processes of healing and recovery. It told us of a " vital force " or " vital principle " to the operation of which these processes are due, and of the influence of medical and surgical interference in aiding this operation. Vitalism has disappeared from official physiology ; but I believe that the great majority of those engaged in actual medical and surgical practice are still at heart vitalists, and for the simple reason that they must have some sort of creed to correspond, however imperfectly, with the facts they are in contact with.

There are, nevertheless, the clearest reasons for discarding the old vitalism. The vitalists assumed the existence of a so-called vital force independent of physical and chemical influences, but capable of acting upon matter within the living body, and actually doing so in such a way as to cause the phenomena of life to fulfil their characteristic course. It was supposed to be the vital force that shepherds molecules into the specific arrangements which they assume in organic structures; that shepherds them through various normal metabolic processes occurring in living tissues; and that shepherds them in all the processes of organic repair and reproduction. The vital force might therefore be compared to an ideal which, though we ourselves are not conscious of it, is always actively realising itself in the living structure of an organism, and thus controlling the blind mechanism of physical and chemical action.

When, however, vitalism was put to the test of experimental investigation, it was found invariably that what was put down to the influence of the vital force depends on the operation of apparent physical and chemical influences of some kind. As examples of such influences we may take the presence, in certain concentrations, of oxygen, of different salts, or various organic substances, or the existence of a certain body-temperature.

It is thus evident that no justification exists for assuming that there is present in the tissues of living organisms some kind of agent which acts independently of what we call physical and chemical conditions. The evidence is all the other way ; and this fact is inconsistent with the vitalistic hypothesis. We may rest assured that vitalism in its old sense has finally disappeared from physiology.

If, however, we turn round and ask whether the mechanistic physiology can furnish any better interpretation of the phenomena which gave rise to the theory of vital force, the answer, to my mind, is emphatically a negative one. What intelligible account can the mechanistic theory of life give of the phenomena of recovery from disease and injuries ? Simply none at all, except that these phenomena are so complex and strange that as yet we cannot understand them. It is exactly the same with the closely related phenomena of reproduction. We cannot by any stretch of imagination conceive a delicate and complex mechanism which is capable, like a living organism, of reproducing itself indefinitely often.

On their practical therapeutic side medicine and surgery are therefore left without definite general principles, or " institutes," to use the old-fashioned term. Physics, chemistry, normal and pathological anatomy, bacteriology, and physiology are all of the greatest help in diagnosis and in the avoidance of disease and injury, but among them they do not supply the missing " institutes "; and the consequences of this defect are very serious. Nevertheless, I am one of those who still believe that the institutes of medicine are to be found in physiology if only we understand and teach physiology rightly; also that anatomy, pathology, pharmacology, and general biology have a latent claim to rank with physiology in this respect.

We may say without serious misrepresentation that the usual present-day view of physiologists is that physiology aims at gradually revealing the mechanism of life—in other words, that it aims at investigating the physics and chemistry of life, and might properly be called bio-physics and bio-chemistry. This is a view which I cannot share, and I wish to show you that the proper, and in the main the actual, aim of physiology is very different, and is one which brings physiology into the closest relation, not only with the diagnostic side of practical medicine, but also with the therapeutic and preventive sides. My own connection with preventive medicine on its industrial side has often taught me the inadequacy of mechanistic physiology as a basis for preventive medicine.

Let me first refer shortly to a line of argument which appeals to many, and which seems to justify the view that physiology can be nothing but the application of physics and chemistry to life. In physiology, it is argued, we are dealing with nothing but physical or chemical changes, and in investigating these changes we use precisely the same methods of measurement as in the investigation of other material changes. The same fundamental laws of conservation of matter, of atomic identity, and of energy as apply in the inorganic world, are found by experiment to apply also in connection with life. We are bound, therefore, to regard life as only an example, however complex, of ordinary material changes, and subject, therefore, to the ordinary laws of material change. All we can do is to investigate life from this standpoint. There might, of course, be continuous miracles happening in connection with life. If so, they are at any rate outside the sphere of science. Possibly the extraordinary phenomena of reproduction and recovery from disease and injury do involve an unintelligible or miraculous element ; but though we cannot at present see any possibility of accounting for them, no course is open to us except to push physical and chemical investigation as far as we can. In connection with practical medicine also, the remedies which we apply are physical and chemical remedies, so we can only endeavour to interpret their influence by the application of physical and chemical principles.

Now I wish to point out that this is only the intrusion of a particular sort of philosophy into science. More than two thousand years ago Hippocrates, the founder of scientific medicine, and as it seems to me the founder also of scientific biology, made, if we can attribute to him the relevant passages in the Hippocratic writings, a vigorous protest against such intrusion. He based scientific medicine on the observation of life, and I wish to enter a similar claim that physiology must be based on the observation of life, and not on philosophical generalisations derived solely from the study of what we interpret as inorganic phenomena. What physiology is primarily concerned with is not philosophy, but the scientific description, or interpretation, of the phenomena observed in connection with life ; and to interpret them as mere physical and chemical changes is, when we consider their characteristic features, not possible.

The life of an organism is characterised by the persistence of the details of both structure and activity in which its life is expressed. In adult life this persistence manifests itself in the normal structure which anatomy describes and in the normal activities described by physiology. In the transmission of similar characters from one generation to another the same persistence shows itself, and but for it the classification of organisms would be meaningless.

Let us now look more closely at what is

meant by the organic structure and activity which persistently maintain and reproduce themselves. In the first place, it is neither what we call matter nor what we call energy that remains identical. Matter in the physical sense is constantly replacing itself in a living organism and in generation after generation of organisms. Similarly, energy in the physical sense is constantly replacing itself. From the physical standpoint a living organism is a constant flow of certain kinds of matter and energy ; and in the course of this flow the matter and energy are continuously changing. What, then, does the persistence consist in ?

The external form of an animal varies greatly with varying posture and different individual peculiarities ; but the anatomist can at once refer us to an almost endless network of anatomical relationships which are practically constant in any particular species, and which only vary in points of detail in what we consequently regard as allied species. It is the *relationships* which are persistent, and scientific anatomy concerns itself only with relationships, though these extend to the minutest details visible through the microscope. Anatomy has, however, hitherto confined itself almost entirely to relationships of structure only, and visible after death. To this limitation I shall return later.

The persistence of relationships in activity is not so evident in detail. It is clear enough that the physiological activities of an organism are persistent as a whole. The amount of food consumed, or of air breathed, or of energy liberated in the body, are fairly steady from day to day, and particularly so if we measure the food-consumption in calories, or the oxygen consumed instead of the air merely breathed. Nevertheless, physiological activities appear to be more or less spasmodic, periods of rest alternating with periods of activity, just as in the case of a machine. It is this feature which at first sight seems to justify the comparison of the living body to a complicated piece of machinery, the parts of which are at one time in action and at another time at rest.

In spite of this we always recognise that the body is alive; and the phenomena which medicine and surgery are concerned with remind us of this fact at every turn. It was with the philosopher Descartes, and not with any medical man, that the conception of the body as a mere machine originated. Medicine has little practical use for such a conception. As soon as we look below the surface it becomes evident that the activity of every part of the living body is in reality continuous, and that the difference between so-called activity and so-called rest is only a relative difference in activity. A muscle, or gland, or nerve-fibre at so-called rest is still consuming oxygen and forming carbon dioxide. It is still in active relation with the salts, water, and other substances in the blood, still producing characteristic products of its own activity. We have only to cut off its supply of oxygen or of normal blood in order to realise this through the functional and structural changes which rapidly ensue. We also realise it through the existence of such phenomena as tone in muscles, or the constant afferent influence of all parts of the afferent nervous system. Not even the bones are ever at physiological rest during life ; and of this a surgeon or physician cannot help being aware.

The physiological activities of living tissues are many-sided. During what we call states of activity one side of this activity is temporarily increased, and we can regard spasmodic activity as in the main only a discharge of material, or of energy, which has accumulated. We see instances of this, not only in discharges of organs like the gall-bladder or of various glands or muscles, but also in those of the respiratory centre or heart, or in the extremely rapid multiple discharges of an excited voluntary muscle.

To the physiologist who is trying to see all sides of the activity of living structure that activity is not only many-sided, but continuous. Moreover, it is exquisitely sensitive as regards amount to change in environment. For instance, a barely detectable difference in hydrogen-ion concentration of the blood will, according to its direction, either arrest temporarily the periodic discharges of the respiratory centre, or enormously increase them. It is exactly the same as regards excretion of excess of acid or of alkali by the kidneys, or the formation of ammonia within the body. The delicacy of the reaction of the kidneys to the slightest excess of water, or of chlorides, or of sugar, in the blood, is of the same order.

On the other hand, it is equally evident that the changes of environment to which living structures in the body are immediately exposed are limited in amount, since the composition of the blood bathing these structures is kept remarkably constant. Every year sees important advances in our knowledge, on the one hand of how delicately the composition of the blood is regulated in various directions, and on the other of the supreme importance of this regulation to the normal functioning and structural integrity of every part of the living body. How much of current therapeutics is based on the existence, or supposed existence, of failures in the exactitude of this regulation ?

It seems to me that with all the physiological facts before us we are led to a very different conception of life from that of either the mechanistic physiologists of the second half of last century or the vitalists whom they succeeded. Life is a many-sided activity, including on the one hand the action of the environment in contact with the tissue elements, and on the other the action of the tissue elements themselves. The action of the environment seems to determine both the specific structure and the specific activities of the tissue elements, but the tissue elements at the same time determine the specific nature and action of the environment, so that we cannot say finally that either is exclusively acting on the other. We cannot even say that they are mutually acting on one another, since apart from their active relationships they are completely changed. We can thus know nothing of either by itself. In other words, the relationship of what we distinguish as structure, environment, and activity is of the essence of what we are observing ; and in the persistency of these relationships we find what is analogous to the persistency of anatomical relationships.

As illustrating this statement I shall try to paint a biological picture of living blood. We are all familiar with the physical and chemical picture of blood as we see it under the microscope or in a test-tube, or with the mind's eye in the light of the molecular theory and the kinetic theory of liquids. It is simply an aggregate of molecules and larger molecular aggregates such as the blood-corpuscles ; and the molecules are moving with great velocity in every conceivable direction, jostling one another promiscuously, and are only prevented from flying off into space by the molecular attraction which pulls them up at the surface of the liquid. Order there is none, and definite structure there is none, in this aggregate.

Now let us look at the biological picture. The living blood forms a network extending, like the network of the nervous system, into every part of the body, but without dead ends, unless we include with the vascular system that morphological offshoot of it which we call the lymphatic system. This network is practically the same from day to day, and has practically a constant total volume or mass, and constant total chemical composition. But at different parts of the network there are very distinct differences of composition. These differences, small though they may seem to a chemist, are of supreme physiological importance, and, like the network itself, are persistent. As we trace the network through a muscle, for instance, the oxygen concentration and the sugar concentration diminish, while the concentrations of carbon dioxide, water, and other substances rise. As we trace the network through the lungs, or kidneys, or the liver, or any other organ or tissue, we find corresponding regular changes in concentration. We thus realise that the living blood, unlike the blood in the test-tube, has a definite and abiding structure, analogous to the structure of, say, the nervous system.

It is evident that this constant structure is an expression of constant physiological co-ordination, in both the general circulation and the local circulation, with other activities. If we interfere with either the heart, or the vaso-motor regulation, or the fine local regulations in every part, the structure changes ; and at death it disappears completely. The structure depends equally upon the physiological activity of the tissues. If, for instance, their activity is annulled by the presence of a trace of hydrocyanic acid, the structure is in a flash completely altered. Like other living structures it is a physical and chemical flux ; but the blood in the living body is, nevertheless, a living structure actively maintained.

We can either, with Claude Bernard, regard the blood as the internal environment of the body, or we can regard it as part of the living structure of the body. In either case, however, we are dealing with actively persistent relationships. Through the blood, moreover, the body is chemically in relation with the external environment ; and in the long run this relationship also is actively persistent. The body does not respond passively to what we interpret as the physical and chemical conditions in the environment, but actively determines the manner in which these conditions influence it. In the outcome we can trace the actively persistent relationships, which thus extend over the environment. Just as the biological picture of the blood is different from the physical and chemical picture, so the biological picture of the environment is different from the physical and chemical one. We can see both of these pictures clearly, but we cannot yet see what their ultimate connection is. Following Locke's example, we might call the physical picture primary and the biological secondary ; but this only serves to distinguish them.

It is the nature of the specific and persistent relationships between structure, activity, and environment that physiology is progressively investigating and revealing. Like anatomy, therefore, physiology deals with specific and persistent relationships. But whereas anatomy has hitherto confined itself essentially to the specific relationships still discoverable in dead structure, physiology goes farther, and includes the relationships discoverable in connection with living activity and the environment of structure.

I can well remember how, in my early student days, I was inclined to be impatient over the relationships which my anatomical teachers were always speaking of. Why could they not give a straightforward description of what anatomical structures are in themselves, instead of speaking so constantly about their relationships ? This was in reality the same question as the mechanistic physiologists of the latter part of last century put, and they set out to find an answer on the lines of the then existing physics and chemistry. They would assuredly have hesitated had they foreseen the recent developments in physics and chemistry of the principles of relativity and of quantum relationships ; but the physics and chemistry of Galileo, Newton, and Dalton seemed to them to embody finality, and to demand the inclusion of biology in their system. In any case, I am confident that, however little the fact is popularly recognised, the attempt to satisfy this demand by building up a mechanistic physiology has been a definite failure, just as scientific anatomy would have been if it had ceased to lay stress on morphological relationships. For biology the attempted mechanistic description of life does not represent finality. When we see that the phenomena of life embody mutual relationships which are, or tend to be, persistent, we are using the conception of life itself. This, as it seems to me, is the conception which we must make use of in scientific biology. Biology is therefore a science which deals with lives as objective realities. It implies much more than is implied in mechanistic interpretation, which is thus only a preliminary and inadequate interpretation. We always find, however, that this preliminary interpretation is a necessary stage in the advancement of biological interpretation, so that the physical sciences are a necessity in medical study, though medical science is not directly based on them.

The idea that biology deals with all the persistent relationships observable in connection with different forms of life, and not merely with anatomical relationships, places the study of life in a different theoretical world from ordinary physics and chemistry. In other words, biology

32

is an independent science, with different axioms, and different modes of explanation, from those of physics and chemistry. For the present, therefore, the biological and physical sciences are separate, although it looks as if recent developments of physics and chemistry were forging a connecting link.

Let us now glance, in the light of these conclusions, at the sort of explanation which physiology, or, I should prefer to say, biology, can actually furnish. As an example, I may take the physiology of respiration. From a physical and chemical standpoint, respiration is simply a process in which oxygen is taken up from the air, and carbon dioxide discharged into it. From the standpoint of mechanistic physiology, the physiology of respiration embraces all the processes by which the intake and discharge are effected. This manner of regarding respiration does not, however, tell us anything about the relations of respiration to the other phenomena of life, and the persistency of these relationships, though so far as it goes it is of much use.

When we consider as a whole the facts relating to respiration, we find that ventilation of the

c 33

lungs with air and supply of blood to the tissues run closely parallel with intake of oxygen and output of carbon dioxide by the tissues of the living body, the parallelism being secured through what we find to be normal variations in activity of the nervous system governing the respiratory movements and the flow of blood through the body. In this way the composition of the blood is kept normal. We also find that the respiratory movements and the exchange of gases between air and blood in the lungs depend on the maintenance of normal structure in the parts concerned. Hence the whole of the phenomena of respiration express the maintenance of what we call normal structure and normal relation to environment. This normality involves a multitude of conditions, the nature of which we are only learning by degrees. But though we only know these conditions partially, it is evident that they tend to be maintained. Thus the phenomena of respiration are part of the maintenance of normal relations in the phenomena of life, and are just one side of this maintenance.

Hence we must base our conceptions of the physiology of respiration on this fundamental fact. The apparent mechanism of respiration is in reality a mere superficial aspect of the co-ordinated maintenance expressed by the whole life of the organism. The scientific explanation, not only of all the phenomena included under the heading respiratory, but also of the tissue activity which is mirrored in respiratory activity, must thus be in terms of the conception of life as co-ordinated mainten- ance. In other words, it is in the contribution of respiratory phenomena to the maintenance of life that we find their real scientific explanation.

When regarded from this standpoint the phenomena of respiration form a part of what we can truly regard as institutes of medicine. Recovery from injury or disease of the structures concerned in respiration becomes intelligible generally, as well as adaptation or acclimatisa- tion to conditions which are unusual. The therapeutic action of remedies which help respiration at a pinch, and thus hasten ultimate recovery or make it possible, becomes also in- telligible. The general idea that co-ordinated maintenance must be expressed in the pheno- mena of respiration furnishes us also with a fruitful working hypothesis in experimental

work. Such contributions as I have myself
been able to make to the physiology of respiration have been inspired by this working hypothesis, and, I think, illustrate its reliability. Had
I been content with mechanistic interpretation
I should not have suspected the presence of
various defects in existing knowledge, nor known
in what direction to look for them.

Let me give instances of this. When I began
to make observations on the regulation of
breathing I did so with the belief that breathing
is presumably so regulated, in spite of much
apparent contradictory evidence, as to correspond with what is required to maintain constant, or nearly constant, conditions in the
arterial blood, so that lung-ventilation would
run parallel to metabolism in the tissues. This
belief led me to devise a reliable method of
obtaining alveolar air for analysis, with the help
of which Dr. Priestley and I showed that, with
wide variations in such conditions as the amount
of carbon dioxide formed and oxygen consumed
in the body, or the frequency of breathing or
composition or pressure of the inspired air, the
partial pressure of carbon dioxide in the alveolar
air, and therefore in the arterial blood, remains

practically constant, so that the breathing is in reality accurately co-ordinated with tissue metabolism.

To take another instance, Miss Christiansen, Dr. Douglas, and I found, following the same line of expectation, that the alkali available for taking up carbon dioxide in the blood, as shown by its dissociation curve for carbon dioxide, is similarly steady for month after month. At first we got apparent irregularities, but, being sceptical as to their real existence, we found that they were due to changes in the blood after it was shed, and disappeared entirely when fresh blood was always taken. The experimentally determined points then fell pat on the curve every time.

To take one more instance where similar considerations guided us, we found, by a new and exact method based on my former studies of carbon-monoxide poisoning, that when want of oxygen is experienced, as during life at high altitudes, severe muscular work, or carbon-monoxide poisoning, the living layer between the alveolar air and the blood secretes oxygen actively inwards, and thus combats the want of oxygen. Our conclusions on this point

37

have been challenged, but on experimental grounds which, I must frankly say, seem to me thoroughly unsound, as I have elsewhere pointed out in detail.

The idea that active secretion should occur in the lungs is suspect to some physiologists as savouring of vitalism. They imagine that if this could be eliminated, the way would be clear for a mechanistic account of respiratory phenomena. But these phenomena display, in any case, all the characteristic features of life as such, so that mechanistic interpretation of them is impossible. The co-ordinated maintenance which dominates both the activities and the structures concerned in respiration is just as unintelligible from a mechanistic standpoint as are the phenomena of reproduction and healing. The question whether or not active secretion of oxygen occurs in the lungs is simply one for experimental evidence to decide ; and if that evidence had indicated no secretion a mechanistic interpretation of respiration would still have been impossible. Those who in their innocence cling, on theoretical grounds, to a mechanistic conception of the passage inwards of oxygen are straining at a gnat while swallowing a camel.

38

The same considerations as apply to the physiology of respiration apply also to that of nutrition, secretion, circulation, muscular activity, temperature regulation, nervous activity, including that of sense organs, and every other part of physiology with respect to which a considerable body of knowledge exists, though, of course, I cannot illustrate this statement in detail here.

What are the physiological relations on which normal structure depends ? A mechanistic theory tells us nothing as to this, and does not even suggest that there is any question at all. It just assumes the existence of normal physical structure as if it came out of the blue, or were there by a special fiat of a creator. What about all the physiological relations involved in the extraordinarily delicate regulation of breathing ? Do they, too, depend upon delicate nervous structures which have just appeared mysteriously and happen to last during life ? I confess that when I think of the mechanistic theory of life, it is only my personal respect for those who have held it, or still hold it, that prevents me from regarding it with scorn. It seems to me to explain nothing satisfactorily, and always to

39

lead both physiologists and clinicians into dead ends. In any case, I cannot see how it can be made a basis for a science claiming to be called the institutes of medicine ; and this is the matter to which I now wish to return.

As has already been pointed out, the old vitalism brought physiology into some sort of living connection with the therapeutic sides of medicine and surgery, since it suggested a reason why patients recover and wounds heal, and why therapeutic interference helps or renders possible this process. Vitalism is, however, an impossible creed. The creed which, as it seems to me, is the only possible one, is simply that of the fundamental biological ideas which I have tried to explain. They are drawn from direct observation of the nature of life. It is Nature, and not the operation of any supernatural vital force, that we are dealing with in medical work. But in the case of life, Nature appears to us under a different guise from that in which she seems to us to appear in the case of inorganic phenomena. It is just as natural for life to assert itself in face of disease and injury, or unusual conditions, as for it to be continuously asserting itself in face of what, from the stand-

40

point of physical interpretation, are the disturbances of environment to which the living body is ordinarily exposed.

Medicine and surgery are therefore based on biology, and biology represents the institutes of medicine. I have said biology rather than physiology, because the word physiology would seem to exclude both normal and morbid anatomy as well as general biology. But structure, environment, and activity are inseparably united in the conception of life, so that it is impossible to leave out sciences dealing with organic structure. Anatomy was side-tracked by both the vitalistic and mechanistic theories of life. They assumed structure as just given physical structure—put there by a great artificer perhaps, as in the case of the watch with which Paley opened his once-famous argument, or by natural selection, or by the vital force. This physical structure was then merely something for physical and chemical influences, or for the vital force, to play upon. The anatomists were thus left with nothing but the relationships of lifeless structure to work with. But with the passing of both the mechanistic and vitalistic theories all this will be changed. It

41

matters not whether in the investigation of life we use mainly the scalpel, microscope and microtome, or instruments for observing and recording physical changes, or chemical apparatus and reagents of different kinds—it is always life that we are investigating, and the apparatus and reagents employed are only a matter of detail. Future anatomy, both normal and morbid, will certainly set itself to investigate the physiological relationships which are inseparable from structural manifestations, and anatomy, both normal and morbid, will then be just as much an experimental science as is physiology. Its relations to surgery will also be much more intimate and fruitful than at present ; for the surgeon deals with living, not with dead, tissues.

The more we understand of the biological relations of both function and structure, the more easy does it become to detect and understand deviations from the normal, and to suggest methods of meeting the deviations and promoting recovery. Without this understanding we are simply groping in the dark, unable, except by rule of thumb, to diagnose the condition of a patient, or to see how he can be helped.

In connection with disease, injury, and the action of drugs and poisons, physiology passes into pathology and pharmacology, and normal into morbid anatomy. The passage is, however, quite a natural one, and it is still always with biology that we are dealing. It has been my lot to investigate, or come into close contact with, various conditions in connection with which physiology, pathology, and therapeutics meet directly. One of these, to which I may refer for illustration, is defective oxygenation of the blood, whether produced by low atmospheric pressure, low percentages of oxygen in the air, abnormality in the nervous regulation of breathing, bronchitis, emphysema, inflammatory conditions in the lungs, the defects in circulation of heart disease, or the effects of poisons, such as carbon monoxide or nitrites, which interfere with the oxygen-carrying power of the blood. In some of these conditions the mere proof that the patient is suffering from the effects of want of oxygen, and of how this is produced, suggests a remedy at once. This is, for instance, the case where oxygenated air is continuously administered in bad cases of acute poisoning by lung-irritant gases, or, as Meakins in particular has shown, of pneumonia, or capillary bronchitis. A knowledge of the physiology of want of oxygen may also suggest an indirect remedy, as where carbon dioxide or some substance which, like carbon dioxide, produces a slight acidosis, is employed. But it is cure, and not mere temporary alleviation of symptoms, that is aimed at by the remedy. It cures by helping " Nature " over an emergency.

Even where no remedy is applied, and the cause of the want of oxygen still remains, the patient will invariably recover more or less completely if the condition is not too serious. A typical case of this is recovery from mountain sickness without the patient returning from the high altitude which has caused the mountain sickness. There will, moreover, be no mountain sickness at all if the altitude is reached by slow enough stages ; and this is paralleled by the fact that a patient with chronic emphysema or mitral disease, whose blue lips tell a story of imperfectly oxygenated arterial blood or slowed circulation, may nevertheless be practically free from the symptoms of want of oxygen during rest. The organism has been given time, and the want of oxygen has been surmounted. In this the facts are true to the nature of life as I have tried to describe it.

The want of oxygen may, however, have already produced serious damage; and this takes us into the sphere of pathology. A patient who has suffered simply from want of oxygen may not recover at once when the want of oxygen is removed, or may remain comatose, and ultimately die. We see this only too often in bad cases of carbon-monoxide poisoning or of pneumonia or bronchitis, where acute want of oxygen has been for a considerable time unrelieved. But even where very serious pathological changes have been produced, the patient will, when the want of oxygen is removed, usually recover sooner or later. Here again we are only in presence of the nature of life.

Sir James Mackenzie set an example in the matter of studying carefully the early symptoms of disease so as to find means for controlling it before it has advanced too far. In this I am in full sympathy with his ideas; for in reality he was thus attempting to link up more effectively practical medicine with biology—to rescue medicine from the atmosphere of the deadhouse.

It is the nature of life which I have been trying to portray. The nature of life is the " nature " which Hippocrates seems to have first seen clearly and made the basis of his teaching and practice ; the " nature " of which the etymology of the word " physiology " ought always to remind us ; the " nature " of which the conception has run like a golden thread through the history of scientific medicine. I have in this essay done what I can to show that we can find the institutes of scientific medicine in scientific biology.

II

THE UNIVERSE IN ITS BIOLOGICAL ASPECT [1]

DIFFERENT aspects of the universe of our experience have given rise to different branches of science or knowledge. The temporal and spatial aspects have, for instance, given rise to the mathematical sciences, the physical aspects to the physical sciences, and the psychological aspects to the "humanistic" sciences which deal with conscious behaviour.

For ordinary scientific purposes we can separate these aspects, though we can also readily see that they cannot ultimately be separated. What I wish to discuss is the biological aspect, with its corresponding branches of biological science.

Although biology is among the oldest branches of knowledge, and biological ideas played a large part in Greek culture, as represented for instance

[1] Address to the British Institute of Philosophical Studies, January 12, 1932.

47

by Aristotle, yet in modern times biology as a really distinct branch of science has to fight for its acknowledgment. My lecture must therefore perforce be a fighting lecture. If it were true that life can be regarded as no more than a complex physical and chemical process, apart from the mysterious fact of consciousness which may accompany it, then biology would be no more than a branch of the physical sciences. I shall try to show you that this is not so, and that biology can rightly claim to be an independent science, representing its own aspect of experience. In making this claim I must at the same time protest against the assumption made by many writers that the " science " of nature means simply mathematical physics. In the clear and fascinating writings of Sir Arthur Eddington and Sir James Jeans, for instance, this assumption seems to be constantly made ; and biology is treated as if it were, or at least might be, only a complicated, and therefore backward, branch of mathematical physics.[1] To

[1] I may perhaps point out that if we accept Planck's contention (*Nature*, April 18, 1931) that " the conception of wholeness must . . . be introduced into physics, as in biology, to make the orderliness of Nature intelligible and capable of formulation," mathematical physics can be regarded as a backward branch of biology.

48

be more specific, living organisation is treated as if it were only machinery, to the working of which the second law of thermodynamics can be applied legitimately. A complete *petitio principii* is involved in the assumption that the visible and tangible world of our experience must necessarily be regarded as only a physical world.

It seems to me that in the late Renaissance time, when mathematical and physical science burst into activity with living and fruitful ideas, biology was quite unintentionally put on a wrong track. In questioning Nature by experiment and ordinary observation we need to realise what questions can be answered, and what cannot be, because they are meaningless. The success of physicists and chemists with their own questions led biologists to put similar questions in connection with the phenomena of life, and to assume that they are capable of being answered. The result has been, as it seems to me, that though biology has made very striking progress in modern times, it has also suffered from much confusion ; and as one result biologists scarcely know where they are as regards the question whether biology is in

D   49

reality any more than a branch of the physical sciences.

The characteristic feature of life is that living organisms present a highly specific structure and set of activities, reproduced indefinitely often. In the light of detailed investigation it is evident that all the phenomena in a living organism are dependent on its environment. But it is equally evident that the manner of this dependence is, in its turn, dependent on the organism itself, and is, or tends to be, of such a nature that the specific structure and activities of the organism are developed, maintained for a certain time, and sooner or later reproduced from part of its living body. When we examine any part of this living body we find that it is the seat of constant activity of such a nature that from a physical standpoint both its substance and its energy are constantly being lost, but are at the same time constantly being replaced. Thus both the structure and the activities tend to be maintained in the characteristic manner, in spite of the losses.

Not only the general conception which we frame of life, but also the detailed study based on this conception, must correspond with our experience of life. In ordinary physical and chemical study we analyse our experience into that of separable events or processes occurring in separable material units ; and it may at first sight seem that we must be able to do the same with the phenomena of life. Indeed, it is at present usually taken as self-evident that we can do so, and that the phenomena of life can therefore be included as part of a universe which can be so analysed, whether or not a mechanical analysis is possible. In actual fact, however, we can only do so if at the same time we can account in some way for the characteristic features with which biology deals.

If we persist in the attempt to analyse the phenomena into separable events or processes, we are either driven into the vitalistic assumption that a special influence, which has been called the vital principle, or by various other names, is determining the phenomena within an organism in such a manner as to give them their specific character, or else into the mechanistic conception that the specific character is an appearance dependent on extremely definite and complex physico-chemical structure in living organisms. Both of these hypotheses are represented in the forms which biological theory has taken since the time of Galileo, but it seems to me that to both of them there are insuperable objections, which I shall now state.

The vitalistic hypothesis, which may be discussed first, seemed to make it possible to retain the physical interpretation of the visible universe, with the one provision that what occurs, or part of what occurs, in living organisms is determined in a special and characteristic manner. As a matter of fact, physicists and chemists were usually inclined to accept vitalism, since they very readily recognised the peculiarities of life, and vitalism seemed to leave them quite unencumbered in what they regarded as their own domain. It was also the prevailing belief among biologists from the seventeenth to the middle of the nineteenth century, and still survives among them to some extent, though often in a disguised form. At the present time the difficulty in framing any mechanistic conception of what are known as quantum phenomena is driving physicists towards a conception very similar to that of vitalism extended to phenomena existing throughout what we at present call the inorganic world.

The vital principle was conceived as something which grows and multiplies within living organisms with their growth and multiplication, death being its disappearance. Its influence was manifested in the otherwise unexplained fact that the characteristic co-ordinated details of living structure and living activities are developed and maintained. It was conceived as an influence constantly guiding the otherwise unco-ordinated or chaotic reactions between the substances present in the body, and between these substances and those present in the environment. The characteristic features of life were therefore due to its influence, and the manner of this influence was specific in each species of organism.

The fatal difficulty associated with vitalism is that observation and experiment have shown with ever-increasing clearness that the supposed influence of the vital principle is dependent on what were admitted by the vitalists to be ordinary physical and chemical conditions in the environment. A lack or excess of something (for instance, oxygen or carbon dioxide) in these conditions, or some abnormality in them, is sufficient, not merely to hinder life for the time, but to pervert or entirely destroy it. This is shown by the discovery and study of all kinds of diseases or abnormalities due to deficiencies or excesses in the environment, of the action of poisons, and of various other facts demonstrating how completely all the influences in living organisms are ultimately dependent on conditions in the environment. In multicellular organisms, moreover, the specific behaviour of each living cell is clearly dependent on the specific character of the environment produced for it by the other cells. With the absence of these environmental conditions the specific behaviour disappears.

In view of all this, biologists have almost unanimously abandoned vitalism as an acknowledged belief, and I do not think that they are ever in the least likely to return to it. But the abandonment of vitalism during the latter half of last century led them, since they still held firmly to the Renaissance ideas as to visible reality, to assume that a physico-chemical or mechanistic interpretation of life must be an ultimate possibility, in which case biology must be regarded as a branch of the physical sciences. Let us now examine this conception. We can do so quite generally, without going much into detail.

The general difficulty which at once confronts the mechanistic conception of life is that of giving any account of the maintained co-ordination which is characteristic of life. The phenomena in a living organism are of such a nature that they are not only co-ordinated in a highly specific manner, but are maintained and reproduced from generation to generation. On the mechanistic interpretation these peculiar characters must be due to great complications of structure within what is called " living matter." In other words, a living organism must be conceived as an elaborately arranged physico-chemical automaton. Descartes, whom Huxley and other representatives of the physico-chemical theory of life acknowledged as their historical leader, stated this general hypothesis very clearly in his short physiological books *De Homine* and *De Formatione Fœtus*. We can further extend this hypothesis by supposing that the elaboration is the result of natural selection, acting over millions of years, and not, as various mechanistic theologians and others inferred, of an act of creation by a God possessing superhuman skill and knowledge of physics and chemistry.

But whether in its purely scientific, or in its theological, form, the mechanistic conception does not cover the facts. What is interpreted on the mechanistic conception as the physico-chemical structure of a living organism is constantly passing away and being renewed. In reproduction of a whole organism this process occurs in a gross manner, so that only a very minute portion of the parent organism may pass into the offspring ; and this may be repeated indefinitely often. The theory of natural selection is, moreover, of no help in a mechanistic theory of heredity, since the fact of heredity, including hereditary transmission of variations, is taken for granted in the theory, and so cannot be accounted for by it. It is mere confusion of thought to suppose that the fact of natural selection contributes to a mechanistic theory of life.

Before detailed study of the metabolism associated with life, attempts at a mechanistic theory of heredity were mainly confined to the reproduction of characteristic form. The type of such attempts was the so-called " box within box " theory, according to which the germ contains a small image of the adult organism. Development was supposed to consist in a mere expansion of this small image to the adult size. All the required physico-chemical complication was thus supposed to be present in the small image, and further far smaller ones within it, to provide for future generations.

When no trace of any such images could be found in the earliest stages of developing organisms, mechanistic theories of development took the form of assuming that in these stages there is present a molecular arrangement or system of the definiteness and complication needed to bring it about that, in response to the nutritional and other stimuli of the environment, the adult organism is developed. This is the form which the mechanistic theory takes at present. I need not enter into the elaborations required in order to bring it into harmony with the mass of microscopical and other observation which has meanwhile accumulated with regard to cells, nuclei, chromosomes and their elements, and sexual union. It is evident that, among all these details, important as they are, we are apt to lose sight of the main thread of argument in the mechanistic theory. That argument is that the germ of an organism must contain a physico-chemical system of such extraordinary complication and definiteness that, in response to the action of its structureless physico-chemical environment, an adult organism is formed with its endless features of minute resemblance to both the form and the metabolic activities of the parent organism or organisms. This structure or system must also be capable of reproduction indefinitely often.

Now when we examine this conception we can very soon see that it contains all the essential defects of the " box within box " conception, as well as greater defects resulting from our far greater knowledge of how characteristic not only the form, but also the activities, of any organism are. Let us suppose that there is such a structure or system within a germ. In sexual reproduction it must in the first place have been produced by some sort of fusion of a male and a female structure. We may picture to ourselves this process as one in which definite portions of a male have been exchanged for corresponding portions of a female structure. A very intelligent ultra-microscopic mechanician might

58

effect this selective exchange, but we can form no conception of how it could be effected by any physico-chemical process. Apart from this preliminary question there is the further and more fundamental question as to how the male or female structure could originate. Many biologists, following the lead of Weismann, have been content to say that the offspring is like the parent because the substance from which the offspring develops is the same in character as that from which the parent has developed, since both originate from the same stock of growing living matter or germ-plasm. But from the mechanistic standpoint this is a mere putting of empty words in place of explanation. By a plasma is ordinarily meant a solution of very large molecules and molecular aggregates, that is to say, a colloidal solution ; and a solution has no definite structure, since its molecules or parts move about freely. A germ on the mechanistic theory must have a quite definite and enormously complex physico-chemical structure, and the structure of the germ of the offspring must have been formed by physico-chemical means in a perfectly definite manner from the parent organism, the germ of the parent organism having within it, in its turn, the molecular machinery for the formation of not only its own adult form, but that of all its direct offspring, including the millions which never develop ; and so on *ad infinitum*. From this we can see that the mechanistic theory of reproduction lands us in absurdities. The attempts to render intelligible in a mechanistic sense how it is that living organisms reproduce what is normal to them seem to me almost childish in their futility. From the mechanistic standpoint reproduction is a miracle ; but such an admission would be a negation of science. The attempt at mechanistic explanation tends to drive us back towards vitalism, with the vital principle as a dumping-place for what seems miraculous.

What we can perhaps realise most clearly in the case of reproduction of a whole organism is, however, no isolated fact in biology ; for reproduction is taking place in all living activity. We can everywhere observe the breaking-down processes, with formation of various end-products, in the ever-present metabolism of living tissues ; but along with these go characteristic processes of reproduction. What is reproduced is living structure and activity with all their delicacy of detail. We can form no coherent mechanistic conception of how it is that the intensely labile structure tends to return always to normality, or, to put the matter differently, how the breaking-down process is so co-ordinated that the building-up process accompanies it. The failure of the mechanistic theory extends over the whole field of the phenomena of life. We can only adhere to this theory if we obstinately close our eyes to facts. The orthodox credulity with which so many writers continue to refer to the " mechanisms " of various living activities is to my mind pathetic in its blind clinging to what has come to be regarded as sacred scientific authority.

Up to a certain point biologists can work on quite comfortably with either mechanistic or vitalistic principles. The mechanists can accept as simply given in experience all of what seem to them the individual physical and chemical facts which the study of life presents ; and they can at the same time accept the characteristic peculiarities of life and account in their minds for them by assuming that further similar study, to which there are no limits whatsoever, will gradually reveal physical and chemical interpretations of them. They can also point to the great apparent progress which has been made in physico-chemical analysis of phenomena on the fringes of life. This progress seems evident so long, but only so long, as no attention is paid to the element of co-ordinated maintenance which enters into all these phenomena. When they look only on this partial picture of life they feel satisfied with mechanistic interpretation. The trouble is, however, that, as has already been pointed out, mechanistic interpretation is quite useless in the interpretation of what is characteristic, namely, the co-ordinated maintenance and reproduction involved in all the apparent physico-chemical phenomena which have been discovered. The more there are of the latter the more hopeless does the problem of accounting physically for the co-ordinated maintenance and reproduction become. Moreover, the farther the attempt at physico-chemical analysis is pushed onward towards intimate phenomena within living structure the more hazy do the results become. Thus the substances which have been produced by or separated from living or dead structures are definite enough in the chemical sense, but within living substance their nature and properties seem undefinable. The " protoplasm," for instance, which Huxley imagined to be a physically and chemically definable substance is, from the physical and chemical standpoints, now only an indefinite name.

The vitalists, on the other hand, are as ready as the mechanists to apply physico-chemical interpretation in the case of everything to which it apparently can be, or has been, applied successfully. They lay stress, however, on the aspects of living activity, where physico-chemical analysis is not only an actual present failure, but shows not the slightest sign of becoming anything else than a failure. These they account for by attributing them to the influence of the " vital principle," which thus becomes a waste-heap for all that cannot be interpreted on mechanistic principles. The trouble of the vitalists is, however, just as serious as that of the mechanists. Whatever influence is attributed to the vital principle can be shown by experiment to depend on the influence of environment, and therefore on what the vitalists have themselves admitted to be physico-chemical

63

in nature. It is only in so far as the vitalists shut their eyes to this fact that vitalism seems at all satisfying ; and the fact is now too evident, particularly to physiologists, to allow overt vitalism to survive.

Since we cannot form a coherent vitalistic or mechanistic conception of life, we must find a different theoretical basis for biology, and we can only find it by looking more closely at the observed facts of life. In life we find that all the phenomena concerned—structure, activity, and active relations with environment—are, or tend towards being, so co-ordinated that they express what is normal for an adult organism. This is the fundamental feature of what we observe. If we attempt to analyse life into various separable events or processes, whether physico-chemical events alone, or such events plus others due to the interfering influence of a " vital principle," we are, as has already been pointed out, confronted by the impossibility of doing so. The analysis can never be carried out, since its nature prevents it from expressing the co-ordination which is everywhere present ; and the failure is specially evident when we consider the phenomena of reproduction. The more closely we consider the phenomena of life, the more clear does it become that we can only describe them in terms of the conception that what we call the life of an organism is something regarded as objective in our experience, and manifests itself in the co-ordinated development and maintenance of normal structure, normal activity, and normal relationship with environment outside what we regard as the living body.

This is no new conception : we find it substantially expressed in Greek thought of over two thousand years ago, and it is always present in our minds, even though since the Renaissance it has hardly been acknowledged scientifically. It has, in fact, just as good a claim to be a " common-sense " conception as has the physical conception of what we perceive. When we say that anything is alive what we mean is that it shows in its structure, activity, and relations with environment a tendency towards development and maintenance of the specific form of unity which a particular form of life implies. A living germ is the incomplete manifestation of such unity—incomplete through its separation from the parent life ; and it therefore develops naturally to the more complete mani-

E
65

festation in the adult form. There is no other kind of explanation of individual development. It is thus vain to look for the explanation of the development of a germ or the maintenance of life at a number of separable points within the body or environment. Life as simply life is the reality which must be assumed in biological interpretation ; and the word " life " is indispensable for denoting what we find. The reality of life implies that spatial arrangement does not mean the separate existences of elements thus arranged.

What, then, is biological explanation, as compared with physical or chemical explanation ? Biological explanation is certainly not physico-chemical analysis, since from the nature of the facts such analysis is impossible. In other words, it is not causal explanation. Its real nature is just the demonstration by observation and experiment that an observed phenomenon comes under the general conception of the life of an organism, since it is something which tends to be maintained in definite relation to the other phenomena of its life—in other words, that the phenomenon is a normal expression of life. We observe innumerable facts with regard to living animals—for instance, the fact that they take up oxygen. When we also find that restriction of oxygen-intake is resisted in various ways, and that if it nevertheless occurs every activity in the body is deranged and minute structure seriously affected, we have definitely shown that what we might simply call a certain transfer of oxygen is an act of physiological respiration, and, as such, an active and normal manifestation of the organism's life. The presence of oxygen in the air breathed and in the blood, the structure of the lungs, the circulation of the blood, and the presence in it of hæmoglobin and other substances, are similar manifestations. These phenomena, to which very many others have been added, and are being added by further investigation, are seen to be connected as the maintenance of a life. The demonstration of this connection constitutes biological explanation of them, and this kind of explanation is what, in actual fact, biological investigation is always aiming at the extension of. Through the advancing demonstration we gain enormously in power of prediction and practical control, wherever we are in presence of biological phenomena.

This is true even if we are only using purely anatomical methods of investigation ; for we are seeking for and finding maintained co-ordinated relationship in structure; and the discovery of this gives us the great powers of prediction which a scientific anatomist possesses. But in seeking out these relationships, anatomists have also always in mind to a greater or less extent the relationship of structures to their activities and to the nature of environment, in accordance with the conception that life is a whole which realises itself, not only in structural arrangement, but also in activity, including the relations between organism and environment. Mere anatomical methods do not, however, suffice for more than a partial realisation of this conception. Physiological methods must be added.

It is useless to regard anatomy as dealing simply with structure, and physiology with its activities ; for the structure with which anatomy actually deals is living and therefore active structure, while change in structure itself is involved in all the activity with which physiology deals. A widespread idea exists that physiology deals with nothing but physical and chemical facts relating to life, and may thus be properly called biophysics and biochemistry. The reasons which make this identification impossible have already been given, but the point involved is one which, with our upbringing in the scientific conceptions which have come down to us from Renaissance times, it is at first hard to grasp. The matter and energy which physical and chemical science present have come to be regarded by us as unquestionable realities apart from our own interpretation of them. It therefore seems natural to us to ask, for instance, what happens to molecules as they enter living substance, or what the immediate source is of the energy which leaves it. Such partial answers as we can get to these questions throw no light on the co-ordinated maintenance observed in what we are endeavouring to describe. The questions we are putting are not capable of being answered, because they involve a presupposition which is inconsistent with our experience of life. This presupposition is that we can analyse the phenomena of life into separable events and processes.

The life of an organism embodies a conception which embraces inseparably the details

69

which it covers, so that when we pass from the physically interpreted to the biologically interpreted world, our standpoint becomes radically different. It is this difference in standpoint which I wish to emphasise in this lecture. In the universe of our experience we find, and I think we shall always find, both kinds of interpretation present. We must realise this fact, and not attempt to gloss it over by vain attempts at compromise, or imaginary deductions of the one method of interpretation from the other.

Though it is true that physico-chemical interpretation of life is impossible, this mere negative fact does not give us biological interpretation. The latter mode of interpretation is already present in our experience, and we have only, by further investigation, to extend its application. In so doing we find that it fits the observations with which biology deals, and gives to biologists an extremely fruitful working conception. With this conception they can work profitably, in place of having to struggle with problems that are insoluble because they involve assumptions which are inconsistent with experience of life.

Let me illustrate this by physiological examples. I shall first take the physiology of renal secretion. If we assume that this must be a process which is ultimately physical, we naturally ask by what mechanism the urine, with its various constituents, is separated from the blood. The mechanism which has always suggested itself is that the kidneys act as some kind of filter. But this theory, in whatever way modified, has been found to be quite unsatisfactory, and we can say the same about all further attempts at mechanistic explanation. The more complex, moreover, such attempts become, the more urgent becomes the further question as to how the mechanism is produced and maintained. Continuation of these attempts is by no means an inspiring ideal, and in any case it now seems evident that any mechanistic conception of how urine is secreted would directly involve a mechanistic explanation of how the structure of the kidneys is developed and maintained. We can, however, put aside as meaningless the search for a mechanistic explanation, and proceed to investigate the manner in which renal secretion expresses the life of the organism. Not only the fact of renal excretion, but the variations in the amount and composition of the urine, then begin to become intelligible physiologically. We find more and more clearly by experiment that in various ways the activity of the kidneys is keeping normal the composition of the blood, intercellular, and intracellular fluids, and so contributing to the normality of other bodily structures and activities ; and we can proceed to investigate from this standpoint the activities of the kidneys and the associated activities of the circulation and of other organs. We are thus furnished with a working theory which inspires experimental investigation in all directions, and is extremely fruitful and important practically, in contrast to the fruitlessness of endeavouring to discover a mechanism of secretion.

As a second example I may take the physiology of blood-circulation. The fact that blood circulates through all parts of the body is physiologically intelligible, because by this means the composition of the blood and other interstitial liquids, and the body-temperature, can be kept normal. The conception of this normality gives a working hypothesis for investigation as to how the circulation is co-ordinated or regulated. Physiologists have proceeded to investigate the manner in which the circulation through various parts of the body maintains conditions of normality, and therefore varies with varying requirements for its maintenance. We can see at once that circulation is only intelligible in relation to knowledge of varying bodily activities, such as breathing, muscular and nervous activity, and activity of various glands. The intelligibility is, however, biological and not physical. If we seek for a physico-chemical explanation of why the heart contracts rhythmically in a certain manner, why the blood-vessels respond as they do to certain stimuli, or why the whole circulatory system develops and maintains itself as it does, we can obtain no definite answer. What we can investigate and progressively understand is the manner in which the circulation fulfils its functions in maintaining what is normal within the body ; and maintenance of normality is just maintenance of a life. In this investigation, just as in the investigation of renal secretion, we require the most exact physical and chemical methods. But what we are always dealing with are not the mere individual results given by

73

these methods, but the maintained relations of these results to other results.

Maintenance of normality is a fact present in all physiological activity, and cannot be analysed into separable physico-chemical processes. This maintenance enters into every observation of life ; and the more we discover as to any part of physiology, the more clearly does the fact appear. This is so in the case of even what may at first sight appear to be grossly mechanical activities, such as the contraction of a muscle or the passage of a nerve-impulse. During a muscular contraction the contracting elements are performing innumerable metabolic cycles, in each of which there is a return to the normal ; and we can say the same of the passage of a nerve-impulse. The living structures as a whole express also the tendency towards development and maintenance of what is normal ; and the uses to which muscles and nerves are put in the living body express the tendency towards maintenance of either a biological normal or the wider " interest " of personality.

The same considerations apply, of course, to sensory phenomena, reflexes, tropisms, etc. It is only by confusion of thought that so many persons imagine that preliminary physical and chemical interpretations of these phenomena can stand when the light of physiological investigation is turned on them. The comparison of reflex physiological action to reflection of light is, for instance, a useful preliminary simile, but soon ceases to be useful to a physiologist, since the co-ordinated metabolism which is characteristic of life is found to enter into all reflex action. While it may be true that since the Renaissance physiologists have set before themselves an ideal of either mechanistic or vitalistic interpretation, it seems to me that the actual progress of physiology has been steadily in the direction of extending the application of the conception of life as always a maintained whole embracing relation to environment.

When we regard the life of an organism as a real objective unity which shows itself in the phenomena of life, we can, by progressive observation and experiment, bring these phenomena into more and more clear scientific order. Organic structure is then no longer an arrangement of self-existent material parts in an environment of similar character, but, along with its environment, the active expression of life ;

75

and organic activity is no longer the passage of self-existent energy from part to part, and between organism and environment, but simply another aspect of the expression of a life. We thus do not artificially separate in theory the structure from the activity, and we recognise the artificiality of separating them. The biological facts which have been discovered fit the conception of life, thus making knowledge of life progressively more extensive. We are also furnished with a conception which stimulates further research, just as fundamental physical conceptions stimulate further research when life is not taken into account.

Since we cannot in theory separate organism from environment, it is evident that biological interpretation is without spatial limitation. It therefore represents a definite interpretation of our whole experience, not a conception which is only applicable to the bodies of living organisms. Hence biology is in the truest sense an independent science, co-equal with mathematical or physical science. Since, however, it covers phenomena which from their very nature can only be interpreted imperfectly by means of physical conceptions, it stands on a higher theoretical level than physical science. In other words, its interpretations take us nearer to reality. For biology the universe is a universe of lives, and not of separable events and processes. Saturated as we still are with Galilean ideas, we commonly regard life as something which is intruded into a surrounding physically interpretable universe, and death of an individual as a cessation of this intrusion. But for biology there is no such intrusion, and death of an individual is only a phenomenon through which development of further life is facilitated. Life represents a deeper interpretation of what is interpreted physically, and the physical world is not something outside life. The facts which physical and chemical investigation reveal in connection with life are interpreted more adequately in biology.

In the extension of biological interpretation we use as raw material experiences or observations which we have at first interpreted physically or chemically. For instance, we observe details which appear at first as if they could be interpreted as mere details of physical structure or physical action; and similarly for what appear as details of chemical composition and reaction. When, however, further investigation shows us that these details are determined, in their relations to one another, with reference to a life, or as an expression of what is normal in the life of an organism, we realise that they cannot actually be interpreted physically or chemically. Nevertheless, it is as apparent physical and chemical phenomena that what we are led, when we put them together, to interpret as phenomena of life appear to us first. In this sense biology is based on physics and chemistry; and unless the provisional physical and chemical observation is sufficient, the biological interpretation will not be accurate. In physiological and morphological work we may require the most delicate of physical and chemical methods. If they do not already exist we have to devise them with the greatest care. Much of my own time and that of other physiologists has been devoted to devising such methods.

The fact that crude data of biology appear as physical and chemical data has led to the widespread misunderstanding that biology can be nothing more than physical and chemical science, and to the still more widespread misunderstanding that, however mysterious a phenomenon of life may be, the only profitable way of investigating it is by assuming provisionally that it can be interpreted physically and chemically. This way, however, leads to no intelligible results, as we have already seen ; and mechanistic physiology is not only extraordinarily barren, but fails completely as a practical working creed, if we regard it as physiology, and not as mere bio-physics or bio-chemistry. It is only through specifically biological interpretation that biology can make progress as a science. The progress of abstract bio-physics or bio-chemistry does not represent that of biology.

Biological interpretation is essentially concerned with function. The whole life of an organism is expressed in the function of any particular part or activity, and just in proportion as we understand the whole life do we understand the function of any particular part or activity. The idea that each part of the body has only one limited function is derived from the conception of the body as a machine. The conception of a whole which is not merely the sum of its parts or activities, but in which their own nature is expressed, became in Renaissance

79

times something foreign to the spirit of natural science, so that it was only in an unacknowledged form that the conception persisted among biologists. The acknowledged form of biological theory was either vitalistic or mechanistic ; and in either of these forms the Aristotelian or Hippocratic conception of a life as a whole, of which it is the nature to express itself in each of its details, was lost. For the Hippocratic tradition and for Aristotle it was just Nature that manifests itself in the phenomena of life.

Though unity is expressed in the phenomena of a life, it is evident that the unity is very imperfect. All sorts of accompanying phenomena seem irrelevant to life, or at least cannot at present be related to it. Because of the imperfection in biological interpretation biology leaves endless scope for physical interpretation, and never tends to abolish it except in so far as it re-interprets phenomena which are found to be related to life. For biological interpretation the life of one organism overlaps that of others, though the association of different lives may express a wider biological unity, as in the association of the lives of different cells in the bodies of higher organisms, or the association of plant life with bacterial and animal forms of life.

We can carry biological interpretation backwards in time to earlier forms of life, and we can extend it to very simple existing forms of life. So-called micro-organisms appear to represent a simpler form of life than do cells ; and it would seem that a cell must be regarded as a colony of simple units of life. The facts which Mendel first discovered in relation to heredity accord well with this conception. An ultra-microscopic virus seems to represent a form of organism which may perhaps be of not more than molecular size. The study of so minute an organism may possibly furnish a link in the extension of biological interpretation into what we at present regard as the inorganic world of molecules and atoms. The discovery of quantum phenomena strongly suggests the possibility of such an extension, which must be regarded as one of the scientific aims of biology. This is a very different aim from the essentially meaningless one of tracing life backwards to conditions which can be interpreted in terms of traditional physical and chemical conceptions. The fact that biology has not yet definitely extended itself into the details of what we at present call the inorganic world, is no argument for the impossibility of this extension. Meanwhile, however, we must never forget that biological interpretation extends over the whole field of our experience, however imperfectly in detail.

The lives of all higher animals are associated with what we recognise as conscious behaviour. In our own bodies we readily distinguish between the structures and activities of which we are aware as under direct conscious control, and mere organic activities and structures such as circulation, digestion, or nervous reflexes, with the corresponding structures. Moreover, such phenomena as hunger, thirst, brightness, colour, sound, odours, tactile sensations, sense of effort, pain, and various emotions are experienced by us whether we will or not. Although we are conscious of them their actual occurrences are not directly under voluntary control. Although, to take another instance, breathing is largely under voluntary control, yet physiological investigation shows that in the long run it is regulated involuntarily in a very exact manner, and without the slightest knowledge on our part of what is effected in breathing.

The unconscious or involuntary features in all these phenomena enter clearly into biology. Even though we are conscious of such phenomena as brightness, they can still be treated from a purely physiological standpoint in so far as we do not take into consideration the fact of their appearing to us as constitutive of perceived objects. We are apt to imagine that such things as brightness or colour can be regarded as running parallel to physically interpreted phenomena. It requires very little investigation to show that this is not the case ; but I have not time to discuss here how, as it seems to me, sensory phenomena necessitate distinctively physiological interpretation.[1]

In conscious behaviour, including both perception and voluntary action, we are in presence of what we quite naturally distinguish from mere life. As already pointed out, we regard any phenomenon of life as expressing in itself the unity of a whole life. But in the case of mere life this unity is only regarded as extending over spatially related phenomena. In the case of conscious behaviour, we are dealing with unity

[1] A short discussion of this point will be found in my book, *The Philosophical Basis of Biology*, p. 87.

extending not only over spatial, but also over temporal, relations. In perceptions or voluntary actions the past and future, unified by the interest which extends over them, are no less expressed directly than the immediate present. The test which we apply when we wish to discover whether an organism is conscious consists in ascertaining whether it learns from each experience, so that past experience is directly represented in present and future behaviour. When unity extends as interest over the past and future, as well as the spatially arranged present, we call the unity personality, in contrast to the blind immediacy of the unity we call life ; while what we distinguish as tending to be maintained in the unity of personality is interpreted as of value.

Biology does not deal with personality, nor with values. The science which deals with them is psychology ; and we cause confusion if we fail to distinguish biology from psychology, just as we cause confusion by failing to distinguish biology from physical science.

In conclusion let me endeavour to state shortly the main point which I have placed before you. It is that in biological science we are, whether we are clearly aware of it or not, regarding the world of our experience from a standpoint which is peculiar to biology and different from that of other sciences, particularly the physical sciences and psychology. It is no mere matter of arbitrary choice that we do so, but because it is the least we can do in the direction of interpreting our experience of life. Biological conceptions are more penetrating than those of the physical sciences. In other words, they take us nearer to reality. We might, by applying psychological conceptions to the phenomena of life, endeavour to penetrate still more deeply towards reality. But in the details with which biology deals there is nothing to necessitate the use of psychological conceptions, except in so far as we actually infer from their behaviour that living organisms are behaving consciously.

Biology is thus an independent science, using its own method of interpreting the world of our experience, and its own method of explanation and prediction, which is not causal. To regard natural science as simply physical science seems to me only a sign of failure to realise an essential aspect of the facts of visible and tangible experience. The universe for biology is a universe of lives, no one of which excludes others spatially, since spatial exclusion is non-existent for life. Biology represents, not a philosophy, but a point of view from which we can profitably regard our universe, just as we do in mathematics or physics. I have tried to indicate the biological point of view, and how, in general, it is actually employed in scientific investigation.

III

THE FOUNDATIONS OF PSYCHOLOGY

THE importance of psychology as a branch of scientific knowledge has been recognised abundantly in recent times, more particularly perhaps in connection with education. But there are still very discordant ideas as to how psychology differs from other sciences, and how far, in its scientific treatment, it is necessary to make use of different conceptions from those used in other sciences. This is what I wish to discuss in the present essay.

We may call psychology the science which deals with conscious experience, this term covering both perception and volition, together with their extension in imagination. Any scientific treatment of the subject must start with as clear a conception as possible of what is implied in conscious experience ; and we must begin by considering this.

Our universe is a perceived or observed

universe. All our knowledge of it embodies perception or observation, whether direct or as extended in imagination. We cannot jump out of our skin of perception to a world which is beyond it. Hence psychology as just defined would, in a very definite sense, embrace all other branches of knowledge, and an analysis of what is implied in perception would embrace all knowledge, as was pointed out by Berkeley. Yet it would seem absurd to suppose that knowledge represents mere individual perception ; and, as we shall see, perception is in ultimate analysis much more than this. Perception and volition can, however, be treated for scientific purposes as individual conscious experience, or as that of groups of individuals ; and it is in this narrower and artificial sense that psychology as ordinarily understood deals with perception and volition.

We can regard our experience apart from the fact of its being perceived and of its participation in voluntary behaviour. In the natural sciences, for instance, we do not directly consider the fact that what we are dealing with belongs to conscious experience. Psychology deals with conscious experience as such, so that in psychology we have to consider what is specifically implied in conscious experience.

When we are aware of what is either perceived or willed we are aware of it as related to other elements, without definite limit, in our experience. Thus imagination enters into the very being of each element of our experience. As Kant pointed out, unrelated perceptions or sensations mean nothing. On this point Kant's reasoning is fundamental, and is self-evident so soon as we seriously consider what perception implies.

Each element enters also into what we call our interest ; and interest is defined in what we are aware of as our constant endeavour to maintain and develop a co-ordinated whole embodying what is of value to us, and which is maintained through the endeavour. Effort is thus implied in perception as well as in volition, since the interest implied in perception implies also the effort to maintain it. It is thus in virtue of effort that we perceive what is of value to us ; and what we distinguish as volition is no more than a consummation of this effort. Each element in our experience embodies significance as entering into our maintained and

89

co-ordinated whole of values, and we can call this whole either our interest or our personality.

The co-ordination extends, not only over what is ordered spatially around our bodies, but also over what we look back to as in the past and anticipate in the future. Hence the significance of each element in our experience refers to the past and future, as well as to the present, and the values represented in personality extend over the past and future, not merely over the present. We can disregard the values, and we do so in other branches of knowledge ; but for a science dealing with conscious experience as such, the fact of their presence cannot be disregarded. They cannot be regarded as merely " subjective." Their presence is of the very essence of what is revealed in our universe of experience.

Each perception has an inherent bearing in the maintenance and development of our interest or personality. It has thus a motive character as itself embodying something active, besides passing on into what we distinguish as personal action. This character depends, however, on its relation to the maintenance and development of what is of value, and so cannot be described otherwise than in this relation. Each conscious act has similar relation to what is of value, and so cannot be described as either an isolated event or as a resultant of events isolable in space and time. Conscious experiences cannot be separated from their significance as the embodiment of actively maintained interest or personality. On the other hand interest or personality is nothing apart from the perceptions and voluntary acts in which its maintenance and development are expressed.

We are familiar with attempts to describe conscious experience in a quite different manner, and these attempts may now be considered. It seems in present times natural to us to distinguish the self or ego from a surrounding not-self or non-ego. Over the self we seem to have direct voluntary control, so that it responds as a co-ordinated whole to what affects it from outside, as well as behaving according to its own free inclinations. Over the non-self we seem to have no direct control, and we seem to find no inherent co-ordination in the behaviour of the objects belonging to it. This dualistic conception is not, however, sufficient in its crude form. When we examine into details we seem to find that it is only indirectly, through the action of nerves leading from the brain, and through attached muscles, that we control our bodies. It is also only through nerves leading to the brain that we are in contact with the surrounding world. Hence the self must be situated in the brain. We find, moreover, that impressions transmitted through nerves tend to produce responses which are quite involuntary, just as similar responses or effects are produced in the surrounding external world.

In accordance with this general conception Descartes represented conscious experience as that of a rational soul situated in the brain and independent of the body, but acted upon by it in perception, and acting upon it similarly in voluntary action. This view is a natural consequence of taking for granted the ultimate reality of the surrounding universe as physically interpreted, in accordance with the conception of Galileo and his successors in physical science. The latter conception has come to be regarded as nothing but common sense, easily verifiable in ordinary experience and by experiment. Since the conception of the body as a physico-chemical system or machine gives no account of rational and conscious behaviour, we are apparently driven into the assumption of an independent soul. Psychology thus seems to become a science dealing with the nature and behaviour of a soul so conceived. We find this conception of psychology very firmly embedded in existing orthodox theology.

Such a science is, however, empty of content. The soul, so conceived, receives through the body impressions of different sorts acting as incitements or inhibitions of different kinds of action, and registering their occurrences as bodily traces through which continuously active memory is constituted. But it is from the external world, including parts of the physical organism itself, that all the impressions and incitations to or against action originate. Hence if we hold to our conception of the physical universe the conception of an independent soul melts away, becoming no more than a conscious accompaniment of certain physical processes in the brain. For every perception and conscious action we can apparently assign or imagine a physical cause, and the conception of an independent soul or will becomes meaningless. Psychology now seems to become no more than mechanistic physiology, with the mysterious accompaniment of consciousness—a purely subjective phenomenon—in the case of certain physical phenomena occurring within the brain.

This conception of psychology is materialism, is very widely prevalent at present, and is represented as in a peculiar sense scientific, though it naturally repels us, and seems inconsistent with much else which we commonly accept. But the question is, not whether we dislike such a conception, but whether it represents truth. In this connection it seems to me useless to appeal to an innate sense that our wills are free to choose : for all that we seem to discover is conflict between different motives or incitements originating from our environment or our own bodies, and the fact that one motive proves stronger than others.

When, however, we reconsider the facts of conscious experience, as previously described above, we can see that the whole structure of the Galilean or Cartesian conception of the universe which we see and feel becomes untenable, and with it the apparent development of psychology dependent on it. So far from that universe being capable, except for certain

94

limited practical purposes, of interpretation as Galileo and his scientific successors imagined, it is a perceived and co-ordinated universe of interest or personality and values. The Galilean conception assumes that it can be separated from ourselves and our activities ; but it cannot be thus separated. It may seem that we can verify by observation and experiment the physically interpreted universe. And so in a sense we can ; but only if at the same time we ignore the facts that it is a perceived world, and the embodiment of actively maintained values co-ordinated as personality. When we take these facts into consideration our universe becomes an embodiment of personality—in other words, a spiritual world. The Galilean or Cartesian external world then appears as something which is merely ideal. In the apparent impressions received from a physical environment or present in that environment itself, we find co-ordinated manifestations of personality, as well as in the apparent physical responses to impressions. Neither perceptions nor conscious acts of will can by any possibility be described as mere isolated impressions or responses to them. Their place in personality

95

is inherent in them. The physically interpreted universe is only a very partial representation of the universe of our experience, and for the study of psychology is quite insufficient. What Western civilisation has come to accept as a common-sense physical universe represents a wholesale abstraction from actual experience.

Psychology is the branch of knowledge which deals with our experience when we do not ignore the fact of its being perceived experience, the embodiment of personality. Psychology thus deals with what we call a spiritual universe, and if we have provisionally interpreted our universe physically or biologically, re-interprets it spiritually. The universe for psychology is the same universe as we interpret physically for the limited purposes of physical science, and biologically for those of biological science, but we are only confusing ourselves if we regard the physically or biologically interpreted universe as influencing the spiritual universe, since the physical or biological universe does not exist side by side with the spiritual universe, but is only the same universe regarded abstractly, apart from its spiritual character.

The word " spiritual " is at present very

commonly taken as representing something which exists in separation from what is material. This meaning depends on the attribution of ultimate reality to the universe as physically interpreted. It is not, however, in any such sense that the word " spiritual " is used in this book, but as signifying what is the concrete manifestation of personality.

A man or animal can be regarded provisionally from the standpoint of mere physical interpretation as a physico-chemical system in relation with a surrounding physico-chemical environment. Descartes attempted to represent men and animals in this manner, apart from the essentially shadowy co-presence of consciousness and a soul ; and numerous writers in more recent times have followed his example. His attempt appears extremely unsatisfactory to us. This is not merely because of its crudeness, but because of essential defects, and in the first place because our experience of the behaviour of living organisms and their relations to environment cannot possibly be represented coherently from a mere physical standpoint, as was pointed out in detail in the previous essay.

The man or animal can also be regarded provisionally from the biological standpoint as no more than a living organism in relation with its own environment. The use of the biological conception of life makes it possible for us to describe coherently much which could not be described in physico-chemical terms ; but the description is only a less imperfect one of what we had attempted to describe physically. The provisional biological description cannot express the fact that co-ordinated unity, extending over the past and reaching out over the future, as the maintenance of interest and its constituent values, is embodied in the perceptions and actions of the man or animal, if, at least, we attribute conscious experience to the animal. This is what we imply when we interpret psychologically or attribute conscious personality or conscious behaviour to the man or animal. It is only in so far as we ignore what makes psychological interpretation necessary that we can interpret the behaviour biologically.

The mere fact of perception or conscious action implies the fact of unity extending over both temporal and spatial relations, so that each distinguishable element in what is perceived or willed expresses relation to other elements as participating in a co-ordinated and actively maintained whole of personality. Imagination is present in each element. What is seen or felt is seen or felt as embodying active interest extending over the past and future, as well as over what is arranged spatially around.

We can abstract in thought from the interest and values of what we experience, and from its biological aspects, so that only physically interpreted experience is left. Even so, however, this abstract world is a world of relativity, and so implies unity extending over the related phenomena. Thus, though the physically interpreted universe is ordinarily regarded as a universe of self-existent matter and energy, as a perceived physical universe it embodies unity, called by Kant the synthetic unity of apperception. For Kant this unity was only artificially embodied in each element of our experience. For him space and time were rigid and unalterable forms into which all the details of our world had to fit. It was Einstein who showed how to take the further step which brought spatial and temporal relations into the unity and into unity with one another.

This is, however, a mere abstract colourless

unity, affording no basis for a scientific treatment of psychology, as Kant himself fully realised. It also affords no basis for a scientific treatment of biology, unless biological phenomena are interpreted as simply physical phenomena, which, as was pointed out in the previous essay, is inconsistent with our experience of life. It is our experience itself which necessitates our interpreting biologically what, when we neglect the fact that they may enter into conscious experience, we call the phenomena of life. And similarly it is our experience itself which necessitates our interpreting psychologically, as expressing personality, all that enters into conscious experience. When we pass to psychological interpretation we have left mere physical or biological interpretation behind. We cannot, therefore, discuss the relation of physico-chemical phenomena to life or personality as if they co-existed with and influenced one another. The physico-chemical, biological, and psychological or spiritual worlds are only the same world at different planes of interpretation.

Let us consider examples of the confusion produced by not realising this. Conscious behaviour is often treated as if it consisted, partly of " rational " behaviour, and partly of a blind manifestation of physiological instincts, dependent on purely physiological or physical conditions. As instances of these we might take hunger, thirst, sexual, or social instincts. Many persons would go farther than this, and interpret rational behaviour as nothing more than the normal functioning of physiological processes, since behaviour ceases to be rational when what can be interpreted as certain forms of serious physiological abnormality are present, such as a sufficient rise of body-temperature, a scarcity of oxygen, or a marked abnormality in the activity of some ductless gland. Death, moreover, comes to all men or animals, and the apparent immediate cause of death in the higher animals is nearly always cutting off of the oxygen supply through failure of the circulation or breathing.

It is certainly true that normal conscious behaviour implies what we can also interpret on a lower plane as normal physiological or physical activity, and that when conscious behaviour becomes abnormal there is abnormality which can also be stated in physical or physiological terms, and often treated medically or surgically in the light furnished by these standpoints. Thus paralysis from a broken limb or from injury to the nervous system, or pain and other symptoms from disease in some organ or part, can be regarded and treated from the standpoints in question, and it would be as useless practically to regard them from a purely psychological standpoint as it is to treat from a purely psychological standpoint our external environment, or not to use force on our fellow-men when appeals to reason fail. Nevertheless, it is from a psychological standpoint that we regard, and from the nature of conscious experience cannot help regarding, both our bodily phenomena and those of our environment, when we regard them as a whole, and do not ignore the fact that they are perceived and enter into our interests. From a mere physical or physiological standpoint they are unintelligible to us. For a doctor his patient is no mere case of physiological abnormality, but a fellow-man whom it is his duty to succour as far as possible. For all of us what is around us is no mere physical universe, but something in which our interest is everywhere involved, so that what is perceived around us enters everywhere into our personalities. It is a universe of personalities that individual psychology, or the psychology of natural groups of persons, deals with, and the " humanistic " branches of knowledge embody this kind of knowledge. The knowledge embodied in the " natural " sciences will always be subordinate in importance to humanistic knowledge, because on the whole the latter embodies a less inadequate presentation of our experience than the former.

Although psychological or spiritual interpretation is more deep-reaching than biological or physical interpretation, the possibility of its application to the details of our experience is only limited. In other words, psychological interpretation is always imperfect in detail ; and we can apply only biological or physical interpretation to details which we cannot interpret psychologically. In this sense even our own bodies, as well as our environment, appear, when regarded in detail, as outside of ourselves. It is characteristic of personality that for it there is always a now, where the realisation of values is imperfect, so constituting new problems and new calls for action. It is also only imperfectly that the problems are solved, with the help of physical and biological interpretation, which from its very nature can only solve them imperfectly, though often well enough for immediate practical purposes. Personality is thus constantly renewing itself and taking fresh form. It represents a continuous struggle against what is relatively unordered or chaotic in our experience ; and when we employ physical or biological interpretation in dealing with our experience this is part of the struggle, so that these interpretations are the tools of personality, devised by it, and very powerful tools, in spite of their essential imperfection.

Hence psychological interpretation never supersedes physical or biological interpretation. There always are, and always will be, abundant details in our experience, where all that we can do is if possible to interpret them and deal with them in the light of physical or biological conceptions, although as conscious experiences they are *ipso facto* interpreted psychologically when they are considered as a whole, and it is the psychological interpretation which unites them. To imagine, however, that we can express psychological in terms, or partial terms, of physical or biological interpretation, is to imagine what from its very nature is impossible.

Such experiences as those of hunger, thirst, sexual, parental, or social impulses are, in so far as they enter into consciousness and take part in conscious behaviour, no mere blind biological phenomena, but participate in the unity of personality, expressing that unity, and held in control through this fact. There is thus nothing degrading about any of them. If, however, they are regarded as influences blindly intruding from " the unconscious " into personality, they are represented as something degrading ; and if personality is represented as merely the playground of blindly acting impulses, the result is a travesty of psychology, such as we find in much present-day popular literature.

Personality is not something up in the air and divorced from ordinary visible, tangible, or felt experience, but present in it everywhere. There is nothing in which personality manifests itself more clearly and strongly than in the love between man and woman, parent and child, countryman and fellow-countryman, or man and fellow-man ; and psychology which does not recognise these and other facts of a similar character fails egregiously as psychology, and often becomes extremely nasty. Whether we are dealing with love or hate we are always dealing with personality.

Psychology can hardly be separated from religion. The reason for this is that our experience is not consistent with itself if we endeavour to represent it as experience of mere individual personality, or as ending or beginning abruptly. We find that the fact of moral obligation is constantly present in psychological experience as a striving after truth, goodness, and beauty ; but they represent values which are unintelligible from the standpoint of mere individual personality. The fact of objective truth, appealing to all men, as a value which is sought after in our experience takes us beyond individual psychology ; and it is the same with the obligation to realise and recognise goodness and beauty. As values, however, truth, goodness, and beauty would have no meaning apart from personality. We therefore interpret them as the manifestation within us of divine personality present in all individual personalities.

We have become accustomed to regard truth as the correspondence between our ideas and a world outside us and independent of our experience of it. But, as has been pointed out already, a universe outside our own experience, and therefore outside personality, has no ultimate meaning for us. It is not consistent with the fact of experience being conscious experience ; and conscious experience implies that both perception and volition embody personality, so that our universe of experience is spiritual. In that universe, however, we find the obligation to seek after truth which is truth for all men, and cannot be defined as a manifestation of mere individual personality ; and we are constantly discovering truth of this kind, so that we feel no doubt that behind the psychological world of apparent individual personalities there is an objectively ordered world of truth which, though it must still be a world of personality, is not a world of mere individual personality. We thus recognise the personality of God as present in apparent individual personality, and at the same time recognise that the universe of our experience is the manifestation of God, and owes to this fact all the self-consistency and orderliness which we find in it.

In our obligation to realise goodness in our

own behaviour and our recognition of it in that of others, we are also in presence of what appeals to all men, and which we can only interpret as the indwelling and unifying personality of God. It is the same with our recognition of the beauty around us and our sense of obligation to recognise, cherish, protect, and develop it. Neither goodness nor beauty can be regarded as a manifestation of mere individual personality, though their presence, together with that of truth, enters into what might be taken as only individual personality.

Death or birth of an individual is something which is not intelligible to us from the standpoint of mere individual personality. But from the standpoint of religion mere individual personality is unreal, and consequently death and birth of mere individuals are not ultimately real.

For applied psychology, as in education and in other practical applications, it seems to me that the connection of psychology with religion is of the greatest importance. The reality and strength of moral obligation form the backbone of civilisation. Sometimes civilisation is treated as if it consisted in the mere co-ordinated application of scientific knowledge apart from moral obligation in which religion expresses itself. In reality the acquisition and application of scientific knowledge is itself only one side of the moral obligation which shows itself in many other ways. A civilisation not based on moral obligation is a purely imaginary concept.

Just as religion means nothing to us apart from the fact of moral obligation, so moral obligation loses in authority and strength when it is divorced from religion. From a practical standpoint, therefore, psychology can hardly be separated from religion. On the other hand, we must not, in this connection, confuse religion with the details of existing forms of theological belief or obligations derived from them, since these details may have no essential connection with psychology, or even with religion itself.

Education is the development of personality. We can therefore see at once that education is not something which can be imposed from without, and that it does not consist in mere acquisition of information as such, but information of such a character as embodies itself in capacity to use it in the expression of personality. Predominant in such information is that relating to moral obligation—obligation to cherish truth, to cherish the regard for others which we call goodness or charity, and to cherish beauty in all forms. It is through example which appeals to his own personality that the education of a pupil becomes effective, whether that example comes directly from a teacher, from fellow-pupils, or from the introduction to literature, history, art, and science in their widest sense. Even in the more technical forms of education it is the obligation to become useful that is the inspiring influence. The importance of good teaching for a nation's stability and strength can hardly be exaggerated.

Moral obligation is also the essential basis of industrial, social, and political activity. The capital invested in industry or in social or national undertakings would become worthless at once but for the honest and loyal service which makes industrial, social, and national organisation possible. When the spiritual value of this service is not recognised and acted upon, internal troubles become inevitable. Spiritual values encircle us everywhere, and cannot be expressed otherwise than as spiritual values, the expression of personality, and ultimately of divine personality. The mere interpretation of civilisation as the manifestation of physical, biological, or economic principles misses the fundamental fact that civilisation is the expression of divine personality. Included in this expression are the scientific principles themselves, since they are tools which personality has devised for the furtherance of its own values.

The conclusion reached in this essay is that psychology represents a distinct branch of knowledge, in which our experience is interpreted, and can only be interpreted, as the embodiment of personality. This interpretation, however, is never complete in detail, and always leaves scope for relatively imperfect physical or biological interpretation—imperfect because in physical or biological interpretation we cannot take into account, or only take into account very imperfectly or abstractly, the fact that experience is conscious experience. If we attempt to reduce psychological to physical or biological interpretation, either wholly or partly, the result is hopeless confusion. Individual or group psychology, moreover, implies what leads directly to religion.

The account given in this essay of the foundations of psychology is fundamentally at variance with the materialistic assumptions on which a great part of popular psychology is at present based. These assumptions are not consistent with the nature of conscious experience.

IV

RELIGION AND REALISM [1]

WE can define realistic or reasonable religion as religion which is consistent with the rest of our experience. Religion implies the conviction that not only is the universe the manifestation of God, but that God is present in us individually, and the source of all we call good. This conviction implies the further conviction that only in the existence of God do we find reality, so that outside religion there is no realism.

With this conviction many things seem to conflict ; but it has remained as a great human conviction, taking various external forms, and exercising enormous influence on behaviour. I shall try to indicate why it seems to me consistent with our experience as a whole, and in what respects beliefs currently associated with it do not seem to me to be similarly consistent.

[1] Based on a paper read at a meeting of the Modern Churchman's Union, and published afterwards in *The Realist*, January 1930.

The greatest influences opposed to religious belief appear at the present time to be associated with the growth of scientific knowledge. If we accept scientific description as a final description of visible and tangible reality, the reality seems inconsistent with the religious conception of God. What we call the physical world appears as a world of essentially independent things or " bodies," which, though they act on one another, show no essential unity in their existence and behaviour. In this connection it does not matter whether or not we regard mass as an expression of irregularities in space-time. There is, however, another way of regarding visible and tangible reality ; and it seems to me that it is forced upon us by our experience itself. This other way implies that the physical conception is only a practically useful mode of interpreting our experience where detailed knowledge is defective, as it always is.

When we consider our visible and tangible world as a whole we find that it enters into our lives. It participates in the co-ordination which we find in our own lives and those of others. Everything around us participates in that co-ordination. Our environment is our own environment, though it is only in the course of continuous effort that we realise the co-ordination.

Let us compare this general view with what are often presented as the final conclusions of physical science. For ordinary physical science, as formulated in its main outlines by Newton, and developed during the succeeding two centuries, the visible and tangible world is regarded as consisting of self-existent and in-destructible bodies or units of mass, essentially independent of one another, but influencing one another by the communication of equally self-existent and indestructible energy. We find this conception to be of the greatest practical service.

One form which kinetic energy takes is heat. This is the chaotic energy of the extremely small units of mass which, by clear reasoning from experiments, we have come to know as molecules and other elementary particles. When large bodies come into contact with one another much of their energy is converted into heat. Just because heat is energy scattered about chaotically among particles, and tending to scatter itself further among other surrounding particles, we cannot collect it except very imperfectly into directed mechanical energy of ordinary masses of matter, and we cannot so collect it at all unless a difference of temperature (which means an average difference in content of particulate kinetic energy) exists between the bodies concerned in the collection.

Thus there is a tendency for mechanical energy to run down into heat at a uniform temperature. Moreover, the heat tends to radiate away in all directions, leaving bodies cold and inert. The fact that, on the whole, mechanical energy is tending to run down irreversibly to heat, which itself tends to radiate away from our visible universe, is embodied as what has been called the second law of thermo-dynamics. From the second law of thermo-dynamics, the further conclusion has been drawn that the visible universe is tending continuously to run down into a condition in which any activity which has not radiated away is evenly diffused heat.

Now I wish to point out clearly something which does not seem to have been pointed out before. No fact in our experience justifies this further conclusion, though all our experience does support the second law of thermodynamics itself. If, for instance, we consider the solar system, it is clear that we can easily imagine this system losing its heat, and all movement that tends to be converted into heat, but continuing to all eternity to retain its energy of orderly movement. Some colliding star could, it is true, shiver the solar system into its constituent atoms. But what reason have we for supposing that any such event can happen ? There is no reason to think that the orderliness which prevails within the solar system does not also prevail all round it. Moreover, we cannot see how orderly solar or galactic systems could have arisen out of the chaos which we may picture to ourselves as the state of the primitive nebula out of which the sun and all its associated stars originated. The order must have been there in some latent form from primeval times. To say that it must have originated through some excessively improbable chance is no account at all. What we know as to the physical universe presupposes inherent co-ordination in any case. The physical universe appears to us as a universe of atoms, electrons, and protons, but in the very manner of their existence these units imply inherent co-ordination.

All that we can legitimately infer from the second law of thermodynamics is that chaotic energy is gradually being converted into diffused heat and disappearing, including not only the chaotic molecular energy which we regard as heat, but all other forms of energy which, because they are essentially chaotic, are tending to be converted into heat. It is only if we quite illegitimately assume all activity to be essentially chaotic that we can draw the conclusion that because the second law of thermodynamics embodies verifiable experience, our universe, with all that exists in it, is running down to a state in which any activity that remains is nothing but evenly diffused heat. This conclusion is not only inconsistent with the religious conception of reality, but seems to me to be nothing but unfounded mechanistic metaphysics.

In his book on *The Nature of the Physical World*, Eddington has strikingly referred to the second law of thermodynamics as " time's pointer," since thermodynamical processes are irreversible. He also, however, assumes that the second law of thermodynamics implies that everything which we can call organisation is tending to decay. By this unfounded assumption he raises, as it seems to me, insuperable difficulties for the main argument of his book.

As matter cools down, what we call its "specific heat" diminishes progressively; and at very low temperatures this diminution becomes extremely rapid. Now this seems to me to imply that what appeared to be merely chaotic molecular energy, bandied about from particle to particle, loses this apparent character more and more as the temperature falls. A greater and greater part of its particulate energy is found to possess the form, not of removable heat, but of energy so co-ordinated or organised that, like the internal energy within cooled atoms, it does not waste itself on its surroundings.

The conception of energy thus organised has in recent years become perfectly familiar to physicists. An atom is no longer regarded as a unit of essentially inert mass in the Newtonian sense, but as a system of electrons and protons containing enormous stores of energy so organised that it does not waste itself on the environment, or else wastes only a part of it in sudden mutations of characteristically determined amount, generally known as quanta.

When we endeavour to relate the influence of organisation to mechanical determination as interpreted on Newtonian principles, we are up against a difficulty which seems to me insuperable. The conceptions of matter and energy exclude the conception of essentially organised activity. We need a different conception in order to take in the observations relating to organised activity. Nevertheless, we still need the old Newtonian conceptions for ordinary practical purposes in physics. Physicists and mathematicians are at present struggling with this dilemma, which is similar to that which exists if we attempt to reconcile vitalism with a mechanistic interpretation of matter ; but meanwhile I wish to point out once more that the old idea that the second law of thermodynamics implies that our universe is progressing towards a state in which energy becomes either evenly diffused as heat of low temperature or nonexistent in any form can no longer be upheld. It seems to me that the actual general picture presented to us by physical science is of a universe from which chaotic activity of every

sort is progressively disappearing, and that this
picture harmonises with the conception of
biological evolution or the religious conception
of the universe as a progressive manifestation
of God's activity.

Our visible and tangible surroundings consist
not only of the phenomena with which the
physical sciences deal, but also of the phenomena of life. Nevertheless, it has been generally
believed by biologists for some decades that we
can treat the phenomena of life as being in
ultimate analysis physical and chemical phenomena which can be interpreted on the general
mechanical principles laid down by Newton.
This is the so-called mechanistic theory of life,
and it has been, and is being, spread about by
innumerable popular writers as if it represented
established truth. Ever since I was a young
man I have myself combated this theory in
scientific papers and books, as I saw its impossibility. In the minds of most biologists the
only alternative to the mechanistic theory
seemed, however, to be what is called " vitalism."

The vitalists assume that there is present
within the bodies of living organisms something

which interferes with natural physical and chemical processes in such a way as to account for the characteristic manner in which the activities of a living organism are so co-ordinated that the life of the organism is maintained or transmitted to descendants. This is a thoroughly unsound position to take up, as I have often emphasised. Let me say once more, however, that I am not, and never have been, a vitalist. We can easily show by experiment or observation that all the phenomena occurring within the body of a living organism are dependent on surrounding conditions. Vitalism is therefore inconsistent with our experience, and we might seem, as so many biologists have assumed, to be thrown back on the mechanistic theory.

When, however, we endeavour to frame even the barest outlines of a mechanistic conception of life we encounter hopeless confusion, which the leading biologists of the last generation did not realise. We can conceive no mechanism of such a nature that it maintains and reproduces itself indefinitely, as a living organism does. Life cannot possibly be physico-chemical mechanism. The characteristic co-ordination which we observe must be inherent in the phenomena of life ; and this co-ordination shows itself not merely in the relation between part and part in the body of an organism, but in the relation between organism and environment. We cannot possibly interpret the mutual relations of organism and environment mechanically. When we attempt to do so we find that the organism determines, just as much as it is determined by, the environment, and that there stands out in this mutual determination the maintenance of that which we call life. What General Smuts has called " holism " is inherent not merely in living organisms, but also in their spatial environment without any limit, so that no physical world is left outside of life. We are only going round and round in a meaningless circle when we attempt to interpret life mechanically or as related to a physical world outside it.

There is no " explanation " of life : it just appears to us as a fact in our experience, and a fact which is essentially inconsistent with a mechanical conception of our visible and tangible experience. There is and can be no origin of life out of mechanical conditions. Such an origin is self-contradictory. The co-ordination manifested in life is of the essence of reality.

This co-ordination is much more striking and far-reaching than the co-ordination manifested in, say, the Solar System, or the nature of an atom. Biology as a science starts from the conception of life itself, and traces in all directions and without spatial limit the co-ordination which life implies. Biological explanation is simply the tracing of the co-ordination as such in its manifold manifestations.

If we were in any doubt from a purely physical standpoint about the existence of co-ordination in our visible and tangible universe, an extension of the enquiry to the phenomena of life would solve the doubt at once.

This is not vitalism, but something far more thoroughgoing. It is the assertion that mechanical or causal interpretation of our visible and tangible experience is impossible except as a provisional practical expedient. It is also the assertion that natural science does not merely deal with causal interpretation, but also, as from the outset in biology, with the discovery and corresponding interpretation of the co-ordination inherent in our experience. I think I may claim that in my experimental work as a physiologist I have worked consistently along this line.

To get people to think for themselves, and not merely to follow what they regard as authority, is amazingly difficult. The faith in causal explanation in natural science has become so general that anything which is outside that faith appears as if it were incredible ; and people will accept vitalism, or even miraculous or supernatural interference with physical processes, rather than abandon their faith in some sort of causal explanation. The authority of such men as Newton has possessed their minds. Even now, when the physicists themselves are abandoning their old trust in Newtonian principles, it is still very difficult to obtain a hearing for what seems to me the perfectly clear evidence that biological interpretation is not causal interpretation, however necessary preliminary causal interpretations may be to biologists in their search for biological explanations. It is easy to gain a hearing for vitalism, or an acknowledgment of the " mystery of life " ; but to persuade people to consider seriously what life implies is another matter.

In my Gifford Lectures on " The Sciences and Philosophy " I have discussed very fully the position of biology among the sciences : so I shall not say more on this subject now. When, however, we have included the phenomena of mere life in the visible and tangible experience which we are endeavouring to interpret, we have by no means exhausted that experience, since besides mere life, it represents the phenomena of conscious behaviour.

Now, conscious behaviour is a great deal more than what we interpret as mere life. A mere living organism seems to us to behave as if it were always acting on the spur of the moment, blindly behaving in accordance with the co-ordination which expresses itself spatially in the life of either an individual or interdependent individuals. Conscious behaviour is a great deal more than this, and any attempt to describe conscious behaviour in terms of mere life is foredoomed to failure. If, for instance, we attempt to describe conscious behaviour as simply life which is conscious of itself, consciousness being only a mysterious added character not affecting the objective facts, we are not describing the facts of experience, though we are not so very far from describing them as if, with the so-called " behaviourists," we attempt to describe them in merely physical terms of mechanism.

Conscious behaviour is behaviour in which both the past and the future enter directly into the behaviour of the moment. It implies both retrospect and foresight. When we are aware of our experience we are aware of it as implying both a past and a future, and of ourselves as behaving accordingly. We act in the light of both past and future experience. We shape our conduct in the direct light of past experience and what future experience promises to be. In our conduct, moreover, past, future, and present are so co-ordinated that what we call our " interest " is maintained. What is of value to us is maintained in our behaviour, which is thus different from what we regard as the behaviour of a mere organism ; and into our perceptions interest and value enter at every point. What is not of interest to us in some way or another is simply outside the world of our experience.

The test of behaviour which we regard as being conscious is whether it displays both retrospect and foresight in the maintenance of interest or values. Where we do not find evidence of learning from experience and corresponding shaping of behaviour, we do not regard behaviour as conscious.

I wish to emphasise particularly the objective reality of conscious behaviour as such. By no possibility can we interpret it as either mere physical behaviour or mere organic behaviour. It is unmistakably real, and of the essence of our visible and tangible experience. It is not, moreover, the mere maintenance of individual interest and values that we recognise in conscious behaviour, but also the maintenance of far wider interest and values, common to ourselves and others. In this way we transcend what we might at first regard as our own private individuality: we find ourselves in the conscious behaviour of others.

It is a common philosophical illusion to suppose that one individual cannot enter into the conscious behaviour of another, though the mere existence of language, or what we call knowledge, communicable to others and recognised by them as knowledge, contradicts this illusion. The illusion is based on the application to conscious experience of the mechanical or causal interpretation which we commonly make use of for other purposes. That interpretation does not and cannot express the reality which we experience in the fact of conscious behaviour, and not even what we are aware of in the fact of organic behaviour. Motives and perceptions are sometimes treated by philosophical writers as mere causes of behaviour. In ordinary life, however, as in a court of law, we do not treat them in this way. We regard a man as equally responsible for his motives and perceptions as for his actions ; and quite evidently we cannot separate them, since they belong to the interest which is manifested in his conscious behaviour as a whole and continuously.

It is thus unity which extends over time, as well as over space, that expresses itself in conscious behaviour ; and neither in time nor in space is there any limitation to this unity, the details of which we call " values." In our experience of social behaviour we find, moreover, that interest and values are no mere individual interest and values. Interest in truth, in what is right, and what is beautiful, is far more than mere individual interest. This is simply a fundamental fact which each man learns from his own experience. We have to bow down before that fundamental fact. We find ourselves bound up in the standard of conduct and perception which it presents to us. We may say that conscience lays down this standard ; but in any case it takes us far beyond our mere individual selves, while at the same time revealing to us what is present in our apparently individual selves.

The world of conscious behaviour is only another name for what we call the spiritual world ; and that world is within and around us everywhere, without limitation in either space or time, and without leaving anything outside it. What does not come within it is nothing to us. Our world is a perceived world, and as such it embodies the interest and values which our experience reveals to us, and which are common to us. Let us see what this implies.

By our personality we mean all that is concerned in our personal experience. It is a unified whole, because it is unified by the interest which is implied in every part of it, and which refers every part of it to the other parts. Each perception and each motive or action which can be distinguished in it is referable to the other elements without either temporal or spatial limitation. But it has already been pointed out that personality is no mere personality of one individual among others. We find in social life that it unites us and does not separate us. The more fully we realise what personality implies the more closely does it unite us.

It is this, as it seems to me, that brings us to the standpoint of religion. When we realise that it is personality which unites us all, and unites and includes the whole of our experience, we call that personality God, and join in looking up to God and seeking to do His will as revealed to us in our experience. Science, for instance, as pursuit of truth, even if it be only relative truth, is thus part of religion. Before further discussion, however, let us look back on the path which has led us.

We began with the apparent physical world— the world of matter and energy, of causes and effects. The practical usefulness of regarding our experience from this standpoint is evident. By so regarding it we are enabled to predict a great deal : to avoid what would be detrimental to our interest, and to fashion a great part of our experience in accordance with our interest. Yet if we endeavour to take this apparent causal world as a representation of reality itself as revealed in our experience we do not succeed. Even if we confine our survey to what we call the inorganic world, our experience, as was pointed out, will not fit into the causal conception; and this is much more strikingly evident when we extend the survey to biological observation, and still more evident when we consider conscious behaviour. We can clinch the argument by pointing out that all we know is of a perceived world, so that all we know of even the inorganic world is relative to our perception, which itself is guided by our interest.

Must, then, what we have become accustomed to regard as the solid, self-existent physical world be regarded as a mere illusion? We cannot simply dismiss this question as being absurd: we must face it squarely. As it seems to me, the answer to this question is, not that the physical world is unreal, but that it is the real world imperfectly described or interpreted. It sometimes seems to us, perhaps, that for all our endeavours we are up against, and surrounded by, a world of mere mechanical chaos. This is a possible philosophical position; but it is not the position of practical men, or, I think, of ordinary scientific men; and it seems to

me a mere defeatist position. For the engineer,
or manufacturer, or farmer, or mariner, or even
soldier, his environment is not one of chaos, but
of means of livelihood for himself and others ;
and even in pure science what is always present
is the interest of scientific work. I certainly,
for my own part, would not occupy myself in
physiology were I not convinced of its interest,
whether in medicine or in connection with
philosophical and other interests. Nothing
gives greater satisfaction to scientific men than
the practical application of their results, however firmly they may be convinced that they
can be of more use by adhering to pure science
rather than by themselves taking direct part in
some particular application of it.

Thus whatever practical use, in matters of
detail, we make of physical, or causal, conceptions, we are only using them as useful tools in
the realisation of purposes on which they throw
no light at all. We cease to use the tool when it
has done its work. A tool can give us no guidance as to where its use begins or ceases. It is
not a world which can be interpreted physically
or causally that we are concerned with, but the
actual world of our experience. This world

cannot be interpreted causally, as I have already pointed out. An assumed causally interpreted world is only a useful figment of our imagination. Our actual world is a spiritual world, this meaning a world in which values are being realised.

We have invented the various methods of science for our own practical purposes. They make it more easy to see into the future and past and to plan our behaviour in detail. If, however, we imagine that they are more than our own creations for our own practical ends, we are simply bowing down to graven images made by ourselves. Let us, therefore, make all the use we can of the physical conception of our universe. It embodies a view, though only a very partial view, of actual reality, and is a most useful conception for many practical purposes. In this sense, but in this sense alone, it represents reality. It would be madness to discard it because its uses are only limited, and because it has to be discarded when our experience as a whole is taken into consideration.

The same reasoning applies to all the other branches of science. It is, for instance, very useful practically to assume, as we do in ordinary mathematics, that every event is separated from other events in either space or time. We can make endless practical use of this assumption ; and indeed it commonly appears to us as being self-evident fundamental truth. When, however, we attempt to apply it to our experience of life, we find that events in space cannot be separated from one another, since life is essentially a whole. When, moreover, we endeavour to apply it to conscious behaviour, not only does it break down as regards spatial separation, but also as regards separation in time. Even in experimental physics the assumption has recently been crumbling to pieces if we take it as a fundamental assumption : for it has been forced on the attention of physicists that not only is the inorganic world no more than a perceived world, but it has aspects of wholeness similar to those of the organic world.

When we consider the organic world, or world of life, it is evident that though we can get very far in interpreting it with the help of the conception of mere life, we may also be confronted by what is evidently conscious behaviour. This fact interferes with any prediction which could otherwise have been made on purely biological grounds. Here too, therefore, our scientific conception of life turns out to be no more than a useful tool of limited applicability.

When, finally, we turn to our experience of conscious behaviour, we find that it is very useful to treat it as if it were only individual conscious behaviour, the manifestation of individual interest and value. We reach thus the conception of an economic man, with all that pertains to his individual interest and the values which correspond to it. From this conception we pass easily to the conception of an economic State, representing the collective individual interests of its citizens. These are very useful conceptions, which we are constantly applying, just as we do mathematical, or physical, or biological conceptions. Nevertheless, they are only useful tools. As already pointed out, interest and values are not merely individual. Apart from our mere individual interests, there are things which we regard as right and wrong, and the interest and values which they represent override individual or collective interest and values. They, too, are represented in a State, and it will expose itself to all the enormous risks and economic losses of war rather than compromise these higher values. If it will not fight for them when there is no other way it is disgraced, just as an individual is disgraced under similar circumstances ; and disgrace is far worse than defeat. It will, moreover, subject itself to collective economic loss rather than permit suffering to its own individual members through economic or other causes.

I am now approaching the end of my argument. None of the scientific interpretations of our experience are anything better than tools for particular and limited uses ; but the nearer they take us to a spiritual interpretation of experience the less do they become finally unsatisfactory. They lead us up towards a final conception of God as the supreme and only reality, and of God present in each of us as Personality and giving to each of us the only reality which we possess. It is the recognition of this in our conscious behaviour which, as it seems to me, constitutes religion. By recognition I mean no mere intellectual belief of any kind, but a practical recognition influencing our behaviour and our other beliefs, including scientific beliefs, at every point. How religious belief enters into scientific work I have already tried to indicate. If we insist on nothing but truth, nothing but realism, we are led to the standpoint of religion.

Religious belief is evidently inconsistent with philosophical materialism, or indeed with any kind of belief which postulates definite reality apart from the reality of God. We cannot see in detail how God is present in all that appears to us. All that we can see is that this must ultimately be the case. We express this by saying that it is only by faith that we see it. Hence faith comes to play a very large part in religious belief. But it is with absolute fearlessness that true religion faces all the appearances— all the chaos, sin, sorrow, and death which seem to encompass us. As they so appear, they can be nothing more than appearance. Through them there shines the spiritual reality which is supreme. God is present in them all. This is the faith of what we call a simple Christian. It is a charitable faith, and expresses itself in correspondingly charitable conduct ; but it is also a fearless faith, inspiring fearless conduct, and not separating reality from the practical facing of it.

It is also something within us, the direct communion of God, with corresponding direct authority. Mere human authority or evidence from asserted miraculous events does not produce the faith of religion. Nor can this faith result from mere scientific evidence of any kind, since science deals only with partial aspects of our experience.

I wish, in conclusion, to say why it is that persons who, like myself, regard religion as the most important thing in life, are yet unable to belong to existing Churches. The duty of the Church is to keep religion and the omnipotence of God constantly before us, together with the conception of God as the source of all that we call good and true. It might seem, therefore, that all for whom religion is a reality ought to join some existing Church organisation.

For me the difficulty is that there is so much of what seems to be sheer materialism present in the existing creeds and forms of worship that I must remain outside. To those who, like myself, are engaged in scientific work, this is doubtless a more formidable bar than to others ; and everyone must decide a question of this kind for himself. I should like, however, to indicate more definitely what I mean.

In the first place, existing creeds make it

appear that religion derives its authority indirectly from an historical revelation, instead of from a direct revelation. The circumstances connected with the supposed historical revelation are also to a large extent inconsistent with experience, and rest, in addition, on quite unsatisfactory testimony. It is one thing to accept the evidence that Jesus must have been a man who in his life, sayings, and fearless death displayed extraordinary spiritual insight and leadership, but quite another to accept the reported miraculous events that accompanied his life and death. Investigation, where it has been possible, has always shown supposed miraculous events to be based on illusion of some kind ; and even if these events had actually occurred they would simply be very strange events without religious significance.

In the second place, the creeds offer something akin to a future pecuniary reward for religion, and a corresponding penalty for its neglect. This seems to me to be a degradation of religion. From its very nature, religion is its own reward, and the absence of it its own punishment.

A further difficulty is the doctrine of individual immortality, which is connected with the idea of future reward and punishment. Not only is there nothing in the rest of our experience to suggest the existence of individual immortality, but the very idea of it seems to me to be inconsistent with religion. In religion we lose our apparent individual selves in the personality of God, and it is only in our union with God that we are immortal or beyond the apparent vicissitudes of time.

It is because of the difficulty in getting rid of the idea of causal determination as part of reality that religious belief has become bound up with what to me are materialistic, and therefore essentially irreligious, beliefs. God, our universe, and ourselves cannot be regarded as merely related causally. So long as the professed beliefs of religious organisations are bound up with what seems to me to be materialism I cannot join any of them ; but beyond and around them all there is a Church of God, which all may belong to, and which is associated with neither materialism nor belief in miracles.

V

RELIGION AND CURRENT THEOLOGY

OTHER essays in this volume deal with the rational foundations of religion. The present essay is a supplementary one, in which I shall attempt to discuss the very thorny question as to how far various commonly accepted theological beliefs are in reality necessarily associated with religion, or indeed ultimately consistent with it.

It might be thought that there is no real need for such a discussion, and that it would be better avoided, since a discussion of this kind is apt to cause pain to many of those for whom religion is a reality. This is true ; but on the other hand, it seems to me that at the present time religion is perhaps more needed than ever before, and that its influence is enormously weakened among a rapidly increasing number of people through its apparent association with various theological beliefs which appear to be either incredible in face of the general increase in knowledge, or so doubtful and obscure as to produce the impression that religion itself rests on quite insecure foundations. In addition to this, these incredible or doubtful beliefs are so embedded in creeds and forms of worship that persons in all classes are repelled from churches, and the recruitment of sufficiently educated men as clergymen is rendered extremely difficult. I shall venture, therefore, as one whose belief in the need for religion is whole-hearted, to refer, one by one, to theological beliefs which seem to me to obscure religion.

In the first place, I wish to discuss the belief that religion is bound up with miraculous historical events of various kinds. Miraculous events may be defined as events of such a kind as are never met with in ordinary experience. As instances may be taken sudden creation or sudden appearance of reality out of nothing, resurrection of the dead, sudden healing of serious disease or injury, or virgin birth. Records of such alleged occurrences lead inevitably to enquiry as to the validity of both the records themselves and the evidence on which they were based. In both respects the alleged occurrences have failed to stand before enquiry.

The belief that the visible and tangible universe was created suddenly some six thousand years ago is quite inconsistent with geological, archæological, and physical evidence. This is now generally acknowledged ; but the fact that so many representatives of religion have only acknowledged it because they could not help doing so has appeared to compromise religion itself.

The records which have come down to us in the Old and New Testaments of various miraculous events, including both the birth and the resurrection of Jesus, have been shown to be, not first-hand evidence, but no more than traditions accepted by certain persons as true, and often clearly of a composite authorship. The events themselves are such as, if they were recorded in present times, would at once be treated by most persons as merely imaginary, and accepted by no educated person without close scrutiny of the evidence, including enquiry into the competence of any witnesses to describe their experiences correctly. To persons who approach impartially these records of miraculous events the evidence for their actual occurrence is entirely unconvincing ; and in so

far as the acceptance of this evidence is represented as a part of religion the appeal of religion
itself to educated men is greatly weakened.
Religion is essentially associated with belief in
truth, and thus it is in reality from religion itself
that the refusal comes to accept as true what
does not appear to be true.

Belief in miraculous events is reflected in a
commonly accepted attitude towards prayer.
According to this attitude the course of events
may be influenced by miraculous interference,
though not a trace of any such interference can
ever be verified. There is, however, another
attitude towards prayer, and one for which the
efficacy of prayer is very real. On this attitude
prayer is just an acknowledgment and reminder
that in doing our duty, whatever it may be, God
is present in us and with us. It may be that the
duty is something very active, or else merely to
suffer or even face death without any avoidable
pain or trouble to others. This acknowledgment gives inspiration and courage in meeting
trouble and danger, in self-sacrifice for others,
and in performing whatever actions seem right.
Prayer in this sense is therefore a very important and powerful influence in human affairs,

K   145

and we can say the same of other religious ceremonies when they are regarded in the same manner. But prayer for miraculous interference with what is regarded as the physical course of Nature seems to me to be nothing better than an inconsistent mixture of materialism and religion—a partial degradation of the attitude of religion to that of materialistic realism.

The fact that religious persons cling so closely to belief in miraculous events is not, I think, due to mere mental inertia, but to the fear that if beliefs in miraculous events are abandoned there will be practically nothing left of religion. It seems quite clear to me that this fear is only an outcome of the materialism with which theology has become permeated to a greater and greater extent as physical science has developed. If the ordinary visible and tangible universe of our experience were nothing more than the universe as interpreted physically, then it would certainly follow that apart from miraculous events of various kinds, religion would be no more than an illusion.

Miraculous events are sometimes assumed to be such events as are inconsistent with the

146

ordinary physical conception of our universe. But if we accepted this definition we should be forced to admit that miraculous events are constantly occurring. From the traditional physical standpoint the existence of life and that of conscious behaviour are miraculous, and even in what we regard as the inorganic world miraculous events in the same sense are everywhere present. We can, however, repeat and so verify these phenomena, at the same time interpreting them in a manner which renders them intelligible, though not on the basis of traditional physical interpretation. They are thus not miraculous events in the sense that they cannot be repeated and so verified.

In previous essays I have given the reasons for concluding that the visible and tangible universe is a spiritual universe, the manifestation of God's continuous creative activity, and that the physical or biological interpretation of it is only a partial interpretation. Religious interpretation is therefore the final interpretation. We are, moreover, on this view left free to follow scientific interpretation as far as it can lead us, provided that we bear in mind that, although the data of science represent truth, it is only partial truth that they are capable of representing.

Hence religion requires no miraculous events for its support. The belief that it does is to my mind only evidence of infection of theology by materialism. In any case, a belief in miracles can make no man better morally, though such a belief may frighten him into doing, or not doing, certain things. But to shut one's eyes deliberately to the scientific evidence against miracles seems to me an act quite inconsistent with a religion for which God is the God of truth. As a believer in that religion my sympathies are entirely with the scientific investigators and others who find themselves compelled to disbelieve in miracles of the sort referred to ; and as one who believes that the search after truth is a direct revelation within us of God, I can have no sympathy with those who stifle their doubts under authority of any sort.

In the next place, I wish to discuss the idea that our knowledge of religion is dependent on its " inspired " revelation to us from an external divine source. Here, again, it seems to me that the apparent need for an external divine origin to establish religion is due to the infection of theology with a materialism which sees nothing divine in ordinary experience. When, moreover, the historical evidence for the external divine origin is tested critically, the result is completely unsatisfactory. But for its apparent association with particular forms of religious belief no credence whatever would be attached to it. It is simply the absent realisation of the spiritual reality of our universe that has made possible a belief that spiritual reality is only revealed from without, and is an intrusion into our ordinary universe. Spiritual reality is within and around us everywhere, and so soon as we free our minds from materialism this becomes evident.

Were religion not implicit in our very being, along with the perception of moral obligation, no external revelation of it would have any religious meaning for us, though it might inspire us with fear. True religion certainly does not depend on fear, but on realisation of God's existence and love, as revealed to us in our ordinary experience.

The main practical point in this essay is that a belief in miraculous events is an ever-increasing source of weakness to religion. Not only does it cause real conflict between science and apparent religion, but it serves to support the contention that religion is nothing but a remnant of old superstitions. Further than this, our belief in truth, or the objective validity of our experience, is part of our belief in God, so that belief in events which are inconsistent with our experience is also inconsistent with religion.

In former times the association of religion with belief in miracles was far less harmful and less unnatural than at present ; and for rudimentary civilisations this is still true. But in proportion as scientific knowledge has advanced, the association has become more and more harmful to religion. It seems to me that unless our churches become free to get rid of it they are in great danger of ceasing to attract attention, and indeed, ceasing to represent religion at all. Even as things are, it is to a large extent outside the influences of churches or theology which is considered orthodox that we find living religion.

I was brought up in the traditions of Protestant Christianity, and it was through it that religion was presented to me. But I soon found that I could not honestly accept the belief in miraculous events which formed part of the accompanying theology. At the same time, however, I came to realise that apart altogether from belief in miraculous events, religion is something which corresponds with our ordinary personal experience, and that religion, quite apart from these beliefs, is a fundamental element in the advance of civilisation. Without religion we lose the active inspiration, strength, and continuity which are at the root of true civilisation, however crude. Merely to destroy religious belief, however much error and ignorance may be associated with it in backward races or among ill-educated persons, is thus harmful to civilisation, and I have no sympathy with mere destruction of religious beliefs in the name of superior scientific knowledge. In actual fact such knowledge, though in some respects superior, is, as it seems to me, in other and more essential respects inferior.

What, then, is the element of fundamental truth in ordinary Christianity after all beliefs in what is miraculous have been eliminated ? In the previous essays I have referred to the foundation of our belief in God—a belief which is common to Christianity and other forms of religion. Christianity, as it seems to me, has

151

fashioned that belief into a form specially calculated to bring religion into intimate relation with both individual and national behaviour. The distinctive teaching embodied in the Christian tradition is that God is not a being apart from the ordinary world of our experience, but present everywhere in that world in spite of its evil, ignorance, and sorrow. In symbolical language God has taken the sins and sorrows of the world upon Himself, and suffers with us, so that we are not separated from Him through our failures and imperfections or through death. His kingdom is within us, in so far as we strive after what we inwardly recognise as divine.

In more direct language the manifestation of God is not in the attainment of an imaginary good, either now or in the future, but in the striving after what is better. God lives and acts in this constant striving. In experiencing this striving within us, and perceiving it in others and in the Nature of which we are a part, we experience the presence and the love of God.

Christianity, when it is not perverted, is thus very definitely a religion of charity, as well as of truth, goodness, and beauty. It gives hope and courage in presence of what would otherwise seem to be failure or disaster. It also gives national stability, based on the one hand on loyal fellowship among the members of a nation, and on the other hand on friendship and respect towards members of other nations. The presence of God binds nations together in a common civilisation, and the definite religious recognition of this bond gives strength to it, as well as to the social bonds between individuals in each nation.

A later essay will discuss more fully the bearing of religion on death, and on the conception of individual immortality which is commonly associated with religion, just as supposed miraculous historical events are commonly associated with it. It seems to me that the apparent need for a belief in individual immortality is based on an intrusion of materialism into religion, in the sense that we fail to recognise the presence of God in our surroundings, and at the same time fail to recognise that we ourselves are only real as the manifestation of God. In our oneness with God, but not as mere individuals, we are both immortal and free, and it seems to me that when we keep this in view we can be content to meet death when it comes to ourselves or others, resting in God. It is thus that a brave and patriotic soldier meets death, realising that in doing his duty he is one with what is most real in himself.

Along with the conception of our own individual personalities, we must revise the current conception of God as a mere individual person. If our universe is the manifestation of God, it is evident that God is no mere individual person among other persons, but includes within Himself all that is ultimately real in individual persons. Our conception of God becomes thus wider, deeper, and closer to us, than in traditional theology ; and we must regard that theology as presenting to us an inadequate conception of God.

Can we imagine Churches or other religious bodies freed from belief in miraculous events ? It certainly seems to me that we can ; though I do not think that we can imagine them based on anything else than the spiritual traditions in which various nations or bodies of men have been brought up, and which are represented in their literature and art. They must, however, be free to interpret this literature and art in the light of its unalloyed spiritual meaning, and not

154

in a mere literal sense associated with what is incredible or irrelevant.

This seems to me to be the proper aim of what is called the Liberal movement in the Churches, though that movement, in so far as it comes from within existing Churches, is hampered by the binding influences of the letter of existing creeds and appointed formularies. In so far as this aim can be realised, not only will educated persons cease to be repelled from Churches, but Churches or other religious organisations in different countries will come nearer to one another, since mutual understanding will be much easier. Different forms of religion will then be in a similar position to that of the different developments of art or science in different countries. Christians will still be able to use and draw inspiration from the Bible, Christian sacraments, literature, music, buildings, and art generally. All of these will still be needed, but as expressions of spiritual reality which can only be interpreted spiritually.

Beyond all this, religion will come to occupy the secure and indispensable place which it ought to occupy as bringing inspiration, strength, and inward peace to mankind, and stability to civilisation. At present the Churches fail largely in these and other respects, and fail, as it seems to me, through their own halting interpretation of the great truths for which they stand.

From the religious standpoint happiness and contentment are not things which result from welfare in any mere material or biological sense. Were human society freed from all disease or accident, poverty, and overt crime, it might still be very miserable and intolerably dull. The only thing that brings content is the service of God ; and that service can be equally real under the most variable conditions and in any station in life ; for the kingdom of God is within us. God's kingdom is one of loyal service, whatever form the service may take. The religious perception that in that service, apart from its mere outward results, we are one with God, brings inspiration, strength, and inward contentment.

It may be that we are still a long way from a time when religion will be regarded commonly in the manner which has just been indicated ; but I think this time is approaching. The alternative would be a time of prevailing irreligion, the progress of which would be indicated by the extent to which the incredibility of miraculous events had come to be both recognised generally and taken as inconsistent with religion. With this time would come social and national instability, delayed advance of civilisation, and much unhappiness. We can see many signs of this, but I think more signs of a deeper appreciation of spiritual reality and of what religion truly means. It is mainly in the hope of contributing to this deeper insight that I have written the present essay.

VI

MODERN IDOLATRY [1]

THE main contribution which Jewish culture has made to Western civilisation is the conception of one omnipotent God whose manifestation is that of righteousness or goodness and truth. This conception, with its accompanying rejection of idolatry consisting in the recognition of other ultimate powers, appears clearly in the sayings which have survived of the great Hebrew prophets, and is of course embodied in present-day Jewish, Christian, as well as Mohammedan beliefs.

As one brought up in Christian traditions, I appreciate greatly Dr. Mattuck's invitation to me to address you, and I propose to take as my subject Modern Idolatry. In the course of some lectures, now published,[2] which I delivered recently before Dublin University, I said that the

---

[1] An address (revised) to the Liberal Jewish Synagogue, October 25, 1931.

[2] *The Philosophical Basis of Biology*, 1931, p. 105.

158

present age in Western civilisation will apparently come in future to be regarded as a prevailingly idolatrous age, though the form which this idolatry takes is different from the forms met with in previous ages.

The idolatry I referred to is what may be called physico-chemical realism—the recognition, that is to say, of the universe interpreted in terms of the physical sciences as representing in all essential respects ultimate reality, whether or not a spiritual universe is recognised as co-existing with it. Since the times of Galileo, Descartes, and Newton, it has become more and more a prevailing opinion that whatever may be true as to a spiritual world, the universe as represented in the physical sciences is ultimately real. This has come to be generally regarded as nothing but common sense, and to be taken for granted on all hands as self-evident. Nevertheless, it seems to me ultimately irreconcilable, not only with religion, but also with much else which we commonly accept. It is also a belief which has come to oppress us more and more, in proportion as we realise more and more fully its implications.

In the physically interpreted universe man is

159

a mere insignificant item in the physical happenings on a very insignificant planet ; and human activity, even if it somehow represents what is spiritual, seems to count for almost nothing. The boundless expanse around us seems also to reveal nothing of the God of religion ; and if we cling to our belief in God we seem to be doing so in the face of clear evidence, so that religion appears as if it were no more than a mere remnant of old superstitions. In *The Scientific Outlook*, a book recently published by Bertrand Russell (Earl Russell), we find clearly set out, with much literary skill, the implications of physico-chemical realism, which Russell and many others identify with science in general.

It is easy to reason in this way ; and I should like to add that the extreme specialisation of present ordinary university education makes it much easier to do so. Multitudes of persons pass through our universities without obtaining more than the haziest conception of what philosophy consists in, and what the great thinkers of the past have had to say about the universe of our experience when it is considered in its various aspects. I think that in many ways we are paying a very heavy price for this defect in university education, and particularly for resulting defective ideas as to social obligations and religion.

I should be the last to decry the value of the physical sciences or to suggest that they are not dealing with the real universe, or dealing with it in a manner which, so far as it goes, is otherwise than rational and necessary. But I wish to point out in this lecture that physical, including mathematical, interpretation of our experience is, from its very nature, only partial interpretation, and unless this is realised may become, and quite commonly does become, very misleading.

One respect in which physical interpretation is only partial is that it takes no real account of the co-ordinated maintenance which we observe in the phenomena of life. It fails to take account of life because its provisional assumptions prevent it from doing so. It treats our experience as capable of analysis into events or processes which exist separably in space and time, or space-time, and are therefore essentially un-co-ordinated or chaotic, whereas in the phenomena of life experience is revealed which cannot be thus analysed, since lives exist as wholes, and cannot be described or treated scientifically with success, otherwise than as wholes realising themselves in phenomena which are inseparable from their existence in the wholes. As a biologist, I wish to protest most strongly against the identification of science in general with physical science. The attempt, initiated by Descartes, pushed forward by many biologists in the second half of last century, and popularised by eminent writers such as Huxley, to represent life in actual or possible terms of physical conceptions seems to me to have been futile from the outset, and to appear so more and more clearly with every increase in detailed biological knowledge. I shall not, however, discuss this particular subject here, as I have myself done so before, and it has recently been discussed very ably by General Smuts in his remarkable Presidential Address for 1931 to the British Association. He also summarised the evidence that even in what we commonly regard as the inorganic world it is ultimately impossible to carry out any complete analysis into separable events.

On still wider grounds I wish to point out that physical interpretation is only partial. It is only in perception, including perception of our own efforts, that our universe is revealed to us. All that our universe means for us is what is implied in actual or imagined perception or observation. Let us consider what is implied in perception. In accordance with the principles represented in physico-chemical realism perception has to be regarded as a process in which impressions are received from the physical world outside or inside the body, these impressions being transmitted through afferent nerves to the brain, and there, in some way which is still quite mysterious, evoking perception, which thus has its seat in the brain. We find this account still being given by scientific specialists and purveyed on all hands in popular literature, regardless of philosophy ; but it has been riddled by philosophical criticism.

In the first place, if all that we perceive consisted of isolated sense-impressions we should have no right, as Berkeley and Hume pointed out, to infer the existence of an external physical world, or, as Hume added, to infer our own existences as anything more than collections of impressions. Kant, who was celebrated alike as a philosopher and astronomer, added a second and far more fundamental criticism. A mere isolated datum of experience is nothing definable or imaginable. Whatever appears to us in our experience appears as related to other elements in experience—relations of order as regards space and time, of qualitative and quantitative difference, and of causal connection involving identity running through change. Thus we cannot separate individual elements in the world of our experience from the unity implied in our perception of it. Unity embracing the whole of our perceived universe is implied in perception, which is thus not something which can be localised in a brain, but expresses unity which extends over the perceived or imagined world.

Very clearly, however, the unity which is in this way implied in our experience being perceived does not mean that our perceived universe is dependent on mere individual experience. The fact of individual experience as such is a mere detail embraced in the unity. What is actually meant is that in the universe of our experience all-embracing unity is implied, and no mere collection of isolable parts and events. This unity has been called by philosophical writers the Transcendental Unity of Apperception or Self, the Absolute, or God ; but apart from further definition it does not throw light on psychology, nor on the religious conception of God, since it has no definite bearing on conduct or the values embodied in it, as Kant clearly saw.

To reach a less abstract conception we must consider much more closely what is implied in perception and conscious behaviour. Here Kant's reasoning, as was pointed out in particular by his successor Hegel, did not go far enough ; and it was only in a roundabout manner that Kant was able to discuss our conceptions of personality, God, and immortality. On closer examination we find that it belongs to the essence of conscious experience that what we perceive, including our own activity, is of interest, although, as we shall see, this is not mere individual interest. It is only so far as phenomena are of interest that they exist in our experience, whether as perceived or willed. Interest is defined in what we experience as constant co-ordinated effort to realise and maintain what is of value to us, and so enters into what we call our personality. Thus perceived phenomena have a dynamic character as motives in co-ordinated maintenance.

The co-ordination not only extends indefin-

itely around us spatially, so that our actions and
perceptions are unified as regards their spatial
order, but also temporally in the form of retrospect and anticipation, taking the form of active
traditions and ideals. Hence all our experience
involves imagination. Whether we look backward or forward, outward or inward, the persistent and unifying interest of personality is
there, and the corresponding values are an
essential element in the world of our experience.
In so far as we neglect them we are converting
what we perceive into an abstract ideal world.
The world of mere physical interpretation is
only an idealised world—not the world of our
actual experience.

When interest is regarded apart from its conscious extension over the past and future, it
appears as mere organic instinct, and no more
than a manifestation of blind unconscious life in
the strictly biological sense. We are only confusing ourselves, however, if we seek to regard
interest as a mere manifestation of what has been
called " the unconscious." On the contrary,
interest is this assumed unconscious more fully
perceived and understood. We cannot base a
real psychology on the conception of what is

166

merely organic, because in so far as it enters into conscious behaviour any organically interpreted phenomenon shows itself to be more than organic.

The interest and values with which psychology deals have no meaning outside conscious personality ; and the personalities of at least the higher animals appear to us almost as clearly as does human personality. The step in our thought from what we only interpret physically to what we interpret in terms of personality is, however, much greater than that from mere life to personality. The conception of life represents an intermediate step, and is thus of very great importance. But whether we are dealing with mere life or personality, the causal conceptions of physical interpretation are incapable of expressing the facts as perceived.

Regarded in isolation from our experience as a whole, the mathematical, physical, and biological sciences do not deal with interest. They are therefore abstract sciences ; but in actual fact their results take part in the definition, maintenance, and development of interest. Accurate mathematical, physical, and chemical measurements are essential in the definition of interest,

as well as in the definition of life. In the use of
scientific results in our interest they appear,
however, as no longer mere abstract results, but
as transformed by the fact of their contributing
to the maintenance and development of interest.
When we look closely we find that all our science
is based on observation or perception or at least
imagined perception ; so that interest is actually
involved in even what we regard as the purest
and most abstract science. The application of
the principle of relativity to mathematics and
physics embodies a very important step in the
detailed realisation of this fact.

The whole world of our experience is a world
of interest or personality. We cannot get outside personality ; the world of our actual experience is thus a spiritual world. " Das Geist-
ige allein ist das Wirkliche," as Hegel expressed
this. The last chapter of my late brother's
Autobiography expresses the same conclusion.
In the furthest depths of space, or the remotest
past or future, we are still within the spiritual
unity implied in perception ; and this being so,
we need no longer be oppressed by the littleness
of man as compared with the universe around
him. The various gigantic systems of things in

the visible universe and their durations are not outside of the spiritual unity which is also within us. Spiritual reality is all-embracing.

Interest or personality implies that details of what we perceive are of value to us. There would be no coherent experience at all if this experience were not unified as the maintenance of interest embracing the values in which interest is expressed. Interest and its values unite the past and the future, the here and the there ; and our experience interpreted as no more than that of a physical universe of separable events is only an imperfect and idealised interpretation.

While this is true, there is something else which characterises personality ; for the unification is never at all complete, and is only maintained and made less incomplete through continuous ever-present effort. Interest extends over time as well as space, but for it there is always a now where it is passing into new developments, and which gives to personality its free creative actuality in presence of what is not understood, or imperfect, and therefore evil. Physical or biological interpretation can give no account of there being a now dividing the past sharply from the future.

The spiritually undefined or imperfect detail in our experience is always present to us. Into it we are able to bring partial, but only partial, definition by mathematical, physical, and biological interpretation ; and the reason why such interpretation by itself can only be regarded as partial is that it cannot express the element of personality or value in our experience. Nevertheless this imperfect definition is a necessary step towards less imperfect spiritual definition ; and this being so, the data of these sciences have spiritual value, and are not something apart from the spiritual universe, provided that we realise their incompleteness.

We can regard interest as the interest of different individuals or groups of individuals co-existing with one another ; and when so regarded it becomes the subject-matter of ordinary psychology or applied psychology, including various great branches of knowledge which deal with conscious behaviour. It is common to these branches of knowledge that they deal with conscious behaviour, as distinguished from what we treat for scientific purposes as the unconscious behaviour with which the " natural " sciences deal. Over and above individual interest there is, however, what we are familiar with as religion.

Individual interest, or the interest of a natural organisation such as a family, tribe or nation, is regarded as centred spatially among other spatially centred interests ; but beyond these interests, and taking precedence over them, we also recognise our interest in the realisation of truth, goodness of behaviour, and beauty. This interest is not centred at a particular place among other places, but it is present in what we may have taken as different spatially centred interests, and it thereby transforms and enriches them. It does not belong to ourselves as mere individuals or members of an individual society, but unites individual selves and societies, at the same time showing them to be only partial representations of reality. Our personalities regarded as mere individuals or members of societies do not account for it. Yet in it is shown the specific character of personality in unifying and co-ordinating our experience. The values which it represents take also unchallenged precedence over values which we regard as representing only individual interest. This is a fundamental fact in the universe of our experience, and is recognised on all sides practically, in spite of the prevalent confused psychology which purports to explain it away. I think that even in animals we find the presence of moral obligation.

The conviction is common to all men, that what we perceive embodies truth, and refers to a real and objective world, however imperfectly we may interpret it. This conviction unites us correspondingly. We must all bow to truth. It is the same with what we regard as righteousness or beauty.

Since our interest in truth, righteousness, and beauty takes us beyond mere individual personality or group personality, and yet unifies our experience in the same manner as does the interest represented in individual personality, we recognise in it an omnipresent Personality of personalities embracing the whole of our experience—the personality of God. For personality regarded as individual there is a central here among other heres; but for the omnipresent personality of God the here embraces all other heres. Religion seems to me to be just recognition of the manifestation of God in the whole universe of our experience. God is present everywhere; and in our sense of mutual fellowship and of oneness with Nature around us, we realise this. Nature is not merely part of ourselves, but of God. Poetry and Art bring this home to us, as well as the imperfection which is always present, and apart from which poetry and art are unreal. It is the fact of moral obligation that reveals to us the existence of God, as Kant was the first to point out in philosophical language, at the same time pointing out the emptiness of other supposed evidences for God's existence.

The greatest apparent hindrance to religious belief at present is the idea that the universe as interpreted in physical science represents ultimate reality. I have tried to point out how and why this idea is inconsistent with our experience as a whole, however useful and necessary the physical interpretation is to us when we use it as a tool, and not as a philosophy. In the biological, and far more clearly in the psychological, interpretation of our experience we are using much more penetrating and far-reaching ideas, in which physical interpretation is absorbed and transformed. But these ideas are by themselves inadequate for the interpretation of all aspects of

173

our experience. When we look fully at that experience we are led to regard it as embodying the perceptions and will of God, since it embodies effort to perceive fully and will rightly. We can then account for our obligation to seek after truth, goodness, and beauty. This is not something mystical, but profoundly rational.

I am unable to accept the theological conception of God as a perfect being existing apart from all the evil, suffering, and disorder of our universe. This conception seems to me idolatrous, as amounting to recognition of something definite and independent of God. It is in the actual universe of our experience and nowhere else that we find God. The God we find is living and active, constantly creating or evolving order out of indefinite chaos, and present to us in our struggles for truth, right and beauty, as well as when we cease to maintain that struggle, thus incurring the inner disharmony which we then experience. But for the chaos we could not conceive a living and actively creative God. We must regard the chaos as the indefinite background of the definite history which is the progressive manifestation of God. If we consider the conception of a God outside of all suffering and imperfection, we find that it has no real meaning in the world of our experience. It is only in the struggle that the God of religion is revealed to us as a God of Love, Truth, and Beauty.

In the character of Dinah Morris in *Adam Bede* George Eliot has given us a vivid picture, drawn from life, of religion and theology in a simple form. Dinah Morris was a mill-hand, leading an utterly unselfish though inwardly happy life, and bringing help, sympathy, and sweetness wherever she went, but also evoking remorse and repentance among evil doers. She lived in the midst of what she was acutely aware of as sorrow, ignorance, ugliness, and sin; but of all this she says, " I feel, I feel it—infinite love is suffering too—yea, in the fulness of knowledge it suffers, it yearns, it mourns ; and that is a blind self-seeking which wants to be free from the sorrow with which the whole creation groaneth and travaileth. Surely it is not true blessedness to be free from sorrow while there is sorrow and sin in the world. Sorrow is then a part of love, and love does not seek to throw it off."

God's existence is the presupposition of what

is definite in our universe. We can look back to a time when no individual conscious behaviour such as we at present know may have been present in it. It still, however, belonged to the universe of experience ; and the analysis already given of that universe prevents us from regarding it as existing at any time apart from the manifestation of God. The germs of all that we are at present familiar with on our planet, including the life and human personality, must also have been present in what, from the mere physical standpoint, we picture to ourselves as the relative chaos which then existed, but which, from a more adequate standpoint, was the evolving order of God's activity. The conception of evolution seems to me a vital part of religion, but evolution interpreted spiritually as God's creative activity. In any other ultimate sense, evolution seems to me an essentially unphilosophical as well as non-religious conception.

It has been inferred from the physical conception of heat as chaotic kinetic energy of molecules, atoms, and still more elementary portions of matter, that our universe must be running " down " to a state in which any activity which remained would only be of this particular chaotic form. The real basis of the inference is the assumption that our present universe is nothing but a mechanically interpretable and therefore chaotic universe. This assumption is, however, made straightway untenable by the presence in Nature of life and conscious behaviour, in which co-ordinated maintenance as a primary phenomenon is very clearly revealed to us. Apart from this, however, recent advances in physics, in particular the discovery of what are now everywhere recognised by physicists as quantum phenomena, seem to me to have taken away even the apparent physical basis of the assumption in question. According to a quite recent statement of Planck, the originator of the conception of quantum phenomena, " The assumption of complete orderliness in all physical phenomena must always stand ; on the other hand the assumption that the orderly course of a process can be represented by an analysis of it into temporal and spatial components must be dropped. The conception of wholeness must therefore be introduced in physics, as in biology, to make the orderliness of Nature intelligible and capable of formulation " (*Nature*, April 18, 1931). It seems to me, however, that if

M   177

we attempted to remodel physical interpretation on the lines thus indicated, we should have deprived it of its practical usefulness. We must, I think, retain ordinary physical interpretation, but with the acknowledgment that it is only an imperfect interpretation of even inorganic phenomena.

Evolution regarded from the physical standpoint has been represented as a process in which organisation is progressively disappearing. For this interpretation there seems to me to be no real basis. With cooling down through radiation we see everywhere what we must now I think regard as the more and more definite realisation of inherent tendency toward active organisation.

In all definite forms of religion we seem to find present in some form the conception of personal immortality. The absence of this conception would seem in at least modern times to amount to an admission that spiritual existence is either an illusion or is subordinate to a physical universe, the continuous existence of which is never doubted. The whole matter, however, appears very differently when we regard, as it seems to me for the reasons already stated that we must, our whole universe as embodying the manifestation of God, and our individual lives as deriving their only final reality from the manifestation in them of God. On this view the death of an individual is no disappearance of spiritual reality, but something in which God's manifestation is still present. I therefore cannot see that a belief in mere individual immortality forms any real part of religion. I am an old man, to whom death will soon come ; but in proportion as I realise that God lives eternally, and that what is alone real in me is God's manifestation, I cease to fear the end of what is merely individual, and therefore, as such, unreal in my life, or to feel that their deaths have truly separated me from those I have loved, or whose memories I honour.

I know well that what I am saying on this point runs counter to beliefs which are cherished by both Jewish and Christian Communities. But it seems to me that the reason why they are generally cherished is that they seem necessary in view of the belief also generally accepted that the universe as solely interpreted in terms of the physical sciences is real. If this were so we should be driven towards belief in a soul independent of the body, in order to account for the facts of conscious experience. When, however, we realise that physical interpretation is only partial interpretation, and that the universe around us is spiritual, and not merely physical, there is no longer any need for assuming a permanent existence of what we had pictured to ourselves as individual souls.

In view of the persistent and specific co-ordination observed in the phenomena of life it was for long believed that each living organism is the seat of a special influence called the " vital principle," or by various other names. But since it became more and more evident that what was interpreted as a mere physical environment determines all the activities of a living organism, biologists rejected this vitalistic conception, and endeavoured to interpret life as being ultimately a physically interpretable process. In its turn this mode of interpretation has proved untenable ; for closer analysis shows that the environment as it exists for a living organism, together with the organism itself, must, from the biological standpoint, be regarded as an indivisible whole of which each part or activity is an expression.

Similarly, the fact that man behaves rationally,

and not merely as an outcome of blind necessity, led to the conception of the soul or mind or ego as an independent entity which has its seat within the body and guides its activities, possessing also freedom in the sense of not being determined by the non-ego outside itself. On the other hand, it is quite evident that when a man acts rationally he acts from definite motives dependent on his external and internal environment, so that his will is apparently not free. On this controversy philosophical criticism has thrown clear light, and particularly the criticism of Hegel, though I cannot accept his idealistic philosophical system. Human personality, as I have already pointed out, must be regarded as a whole which embraces the environment in which it is expressed, so that motives cannot be regarded as external or causal influences, but belong to personality. Neither in space nor in time is a man's environment outside him. His present spatial environment, his historical relations, his ideals for the future, are all united in his personality ; his world is a spiritual world, and the representation of it as a mere physical or biological world is only a partial and so quite inadequate representation.

When we ask whether the spiritual reality represented in human experience is extinguished at death we have to carry our reasoning farther, and it is in religion that we do so. Looking again at our experience we find in it what cannot be regarded as mere individual experience. Nothing would ever convince us that in whatever way we may interpret our universe it is not a real world independent of our mere individual personalities, so that, however inadequately we may interpret it, it expresses objective truth. Similarly nothing would ever convince us that what we call goodness of conduct and beauty do not possess a value which is equally independent of our individual personalities. Our experience involves the striving after truth, goodness, and beauty as actively operative values which are independent of our individual personalities. It is only for personality that values and their authority have any meaning, and it is therefore a natural and necessary step, which has been taken in one form or another, often very rudimentary, at all stages of culture known to us, to attribute these values to personality which transcends individual personality. Thus we are not merely human but divine. Rudimentary forms of religion have been polytheistic ; but the essential unity of truth, righteousness, and beauty has made polytheism give way to monotheism. Apart from our conception of divine personality our experience would be unintelligible to us. In our recognition of divine values we recognise the personality of God, and at the same time recognise that since God is present in us our mere individual existence is no real existence, and our individual extinction no real extinction. Religion removes the sting of death and individual disaster. In our oneness with God we find immortality and at the same time freedom —the freedom of eternally creative personality.

The idolatry which the Hebrew prophets denounced took the form of polytheism. Present-day idolatry takes the form mainly of attributing ultimate reality to the physically interpreted universe.

It seems to me that those who accept physical interpretation without bearing in mind that it is only partial interpretation are no less idolaters than those whom the Hebrew prophets denounced. At the present time we see multitudes following this form of idolatry, and popular literature is full of it. Orthodox theology, in so far as it recognises a physical, side by side with a spiritual, world, or confuses spiritual with physical interpretation, is also permeated by it. There is no reason, however, why work in science should not be as deeply inspired by religion as any other kind of work ; and with respect to regard for truth, I think it is always so inspired.

Perhaps some of my hearers may think that the reasoning which seems to me to lead to religion is too tortuous, and that at any rate the truths of religion, if they be truths, have not been reached by any process of reasoning, but by way of external revelation, or by mystical perception or instinct. When, however, we appeal to history or anthropology, we do not find that religion has arisen suddenly out of a state in which no religion existed. We find the germs of religion, side by side with the germs of science and philosophy, in the culture of even the most primitive savages ; and the great religious movements in history, like the great scientific movements, have only embodied developments of ideas which existed before. Religious teaching would, moreover, make no lasting appeal to mankind were it not a rational appeal. All that

I have attempted to do is to present the reasoning in a more explicit form, and to free it from
what appear to be irrelevant accompaniments.

The perception, however confused, of spiritual reality, and with it religion, is thousands of
years older than such explicit reasoning as I have
presented. In whatever manner religious conceptions may, however, purport to have been
reached, I am clear that the process of reaching
them has been fundamentally rational, and that
religion is concerned with what is in the fullest
sense real and objective, though the outward
forms which it takes are obscured by much which
must pass away, just like the outward forms of
scientific knowledge.

It is spiritual realism and no mere idealism,
that I have been presenting. I am also not here
to support details of theological belief which
seem to me impossible in view of the advance of
knowledge, but to point to the spiritual reality
which lies behind the outward forms which
religious belief takes. As our knowledge in-
creases, so must our conception of spiritual
reality become enlarged and clearer.

I am speaking to a community who are seeking their way along rational lines which have

guided their people in the past. That way is not the way of any kind of idolatry, but of communion with God in the endeavour to follow the divine commandments written in the very being of ourselves and our universe, and in which communion we find inward peace, courage, and active inspiration.

VII

VALUES IN INDUSTRY [1]

WHEN Sir John Cadman informed me that members of the Council wished me to become your next President, I was very greatly surprised. Although many years ago you definitely took me into your community by electing me an Honorary Member, the possibility of your conferring such an honour on me as making me your President had never entered my mind, and I was well aware of my lack of some of the main qualifications for the duties. As, however, the Council, in spite of this lack, decided to nominate me, I wish to express my deep appreciation of the personal honour it has done me, and to say that I shall do my very best to follow along the pathway of the distinguished men who have preceded me.

It is now nearly thirty years since I first, in conjunction with our honoured Past-President, Sir William Atkinson, read a paper before this

[1] Presidential Address, Institution of Mining Engineers, 1924.

Institution, and began to come into close contact with the mining engineers and others belonging to the mining industry of my country. During these thirty years the contact has been a constantly widening one, leading to many close personal friendships, and, on my part, to a better knowledge and appreciation of my own countrymen. On the scientific side it has also taught me a great deal that I should never have learnt from mere laboratory work.

Though I am not a mining engineer, cooperation with mining engineers has enabled me to realise the work they are doing ; and perhaps the mere fact of my work being mainly in pure science, a different class of work, makes it easier for me to appreciate certain outstanding things which are embodied in the work of this Institution, and which are, and I hope always will be, characteristic of the practical aims and ideals of British mining engineers. I propose, therefore, to take as the subject of this address, " The Values for which the Institution Stands."

When we look back over the volumes of *Transactions* of this Institution and the district Institutes of which it is the union, we realise the great variety of the subjects discussed at meetings,

and the influence these discussions have exerted
in every direction on mining practice. Our
Transactions are, however, distinguished from
those of other professional associations by the
fact that questions concerning the safety and
health of those engaged in the industry we represent bulk very largely in them. The reason
for this is that in mining work dangers of one
sort or another are constantly at hand. It is
only through accurate knowledge, skill, and
constant care for one another's safety, that
those engaged in mining can keep the dangers
at bay. At one time coal-mining in Great
Britain was a relatively dangerous occupation
as measured by the death-rate. It is now,
and has been for many years, one of the occupations in which the death-rate is relatively
low. Low as the average death-rate among
occupied men in this country has, thanks to
advancing civilisation, become, the death-rate
among coal-miners is still lower, in spite of all
the potential dangers of mining work. This is
the result of the knowledge, skill, and traditions
of good workmanship and mutual loyalty, which
have been built up during many generations.
We can look back with pride to the history of

British coal-mining, and look forward with corresponding confidence to continued progress in the future.

Apart from the great trade depression which is the natural result of the enormous destruction of capital during the war, the most serious existing troubles for mining engineers are those connected with what are known as " labour " questions ; and it is partly this fact that has led me to choose my subject. Mining engineers have to face labour troubles along with many other troubles ; but perhaps the labour troubles raise the deepest questions. This Institution stands for the interests and values which the coal-mining engineers of this country have at heart. We are apt to take the nature of these interests and values for granted ; but I think that if we try to define them more clearly, this may be useful in relation to a number of problems, and particularly labour problems.

The capital sum in use, and at the same time at risk, in the undertakings managed by members of this Institution is enormous. If, through inefficient management or other causes, these undertakings ceased to pay a reasonable dividend, that capital would be lost. Let us see

what this would mean. Some of the undertakings might be able to struggle on for a time,
leading a hand-to-mouth life, with no credit to
fall back on for the cost of necessary replace-
ments or improvements ; but this could not last
long. Meanwhile a great many shareholders,
rich and poor, would have lost all benefit from
their savings. To the poor shareholders regarded as individuals this would be a calamity,
to the rich it might be a personal relief from endless cares and responsibilities which accompany
the control of much wealth ; but many persons
dependent on that wealth for their employment
would suffer. What I wish to emphasise, however, is that the country, and on a wider view
other countries, too, would have lost the capital.

Capital means, not merely the power of doing
work, but the power of doing productive work—
work which will afterwards bring a net profit.
Such work is always done on credit, of which
money is the token. In proportion as an undertaking ceases to pay or give evidence of paying
in the future, its credit or capital disappears.
This, unless it has been foreseen and provided
for, means disappearance of national credit or
capital. Power of giving employment over a

circle of which the width cannot be estimated has disappeared, as well as income taxable for both national and local purposes. When we realise the actual responsibility to their fellow-countrymen of those whose duty it is to care for the financial soundness of the operations involved in British colliery undertakings, we see at once how great that responsibility is, and how important it is that sufficiently far-seeing men should bear it, and should not be interfered with by ignorant persons, who are commonly officious in direct proportion to their ignorance.

I think there will be general agreement that one of the values for which this Institution stands is the capital or credit of the coal-mining undertakings of this country. Every improvement in mining practice adds to that capital or prevents its disappearance, and this Institution is constantly engaged in promoting these improvements and spreading the knowledge of them among mining engineers. I think also, however, that it will be strongly felt that the Institution stands at the same time for other values.

From its early beginnings it has certainly stood for safety and health in mining operations ;

and not merely because without a reasonable standard of safety and health mining work would be more expensive, but because care for the safety and health of those employed in mining is part, and a very important part, of the direct duty of a mining engineer. Such contributions as I have myself been able to make towards the work of the Institution have been concerned almost entirely with questions of safety or health. The interest with which these and other similar contributions have been received and discussed, and, indeed, the mere fact that you have asked me to be your President, though I am not otherwise concerned in mining, are sufficient evidence that safety and health stand prominent among the values for which the Institution stands.

There are, however, still other values, and of a less palpable but more comprehensive kind, embodied in the work of members of this Institution ; and it is these other values that contact with the coal-mining industry of my own country has more particularly made me conscious of. The collieries of this country would be quite different places from what they are but for the presence in them of a comradeship capable of dominating all other considerations.

I have often been present at a colliery during some time of trouble or danger ; and it was this comradeship, from highest to lowest, that impressed me most. But whether or not unusual trouble is present, one seems to meet comradeship as one enters the colliery premises or steps into the cage. It is part of the atmosphere of a British pit, and real pitmen seem always to carry some of it round with them, so that the meetings of the Institution abound with it.

Comradeship is just action based on the placing of value upon the interests of neighbours. It carries with it respect, and the very highest kind of respect, for those who show it, whether they be rich or poor, known or unknown. It is comradeship that inspires, and has made, our Institution : comradeship not merely between its members, but also between them and all those engaged in the mining industry. It seems to me that among the values for which this Institution stands those which are embodied in what may be called comradeship are the most important, and in reality embrace the rest.

As collieries have become larger and deeper, so that machinery and organisation of a far more complex character have come into use, the need for scientific knowledge, technical experience, and organising power on the part of mining engineers has constantly increased. So also has the need for seeing to the proper provision above-ground of housing and educational and other facilities for the large number of miners who are required and their families, and to the proper training of mining engineers and colliery officials. But so also, and this perhaps needs emphasis, has the need grown for a more extended realisation of the conception of comradeship or Christian charity in connection with mining. It is not with scientific abstractions called " Labour " and " Capital " that British mining engineers have to work, but with their own fellow-countrymen, their own flesh and blood. These fellow-countrymen will give loyal and efficient service, will face any danger, will forgive imagined or real mistakes, and will take the rough with the smooth, the bad times with the good ; but what they will not tolerate is being treated as if they were mere tools, to be cast aside without compunction. Neither high wages, high dividends, nor welfare schemes will satisfy them in this respect, but only discerning and sympathetic treatment, the treatment of comradeship in a common enterprise—such comradeship as existed in and between all ranks during the war, or such comradeship as is taught in the Gospels.

In saying this, I believe I am saying what all our political parties would subscribe to, however little they speak of it. In any case, I feel confident that I am only describing in words what has been the practice of many eminent mining engineers with whom I have come into close contact, and what corresponds to the underlying sentiment of the Institution as expressed at its ordinary meetings, and still more clearly, perhaps, at its dinners.

There will doubtless always be contentions about wages and other conditions of employment ; but these can be, and indeed have been to a very great extent in the past, carried through in a friendly spirit. The special instability which has shown itself recently in the relations between employers and employed depends, as it seems to me, on the idea that has got abroad that the employed are only units in an economic machine manipulated by so-called capitalists without any real sympathy with or understanding of those employed. All real respect for the supposed economic machine is thus lost. It seems like a thing fit to be kicked or hit with a sledge-hammer whenever occasion arises.

Now I think we have to dig pretty deep to get at the origin of this idea. At first one is apt to blame the mere size of modern industrial undertakings. In a large colliery, for instance, it is impossible to maintain direct contact between the head management and the men employed. With efficient organisation and selection of staff, however, a quite effective indirect contact can be maintained, though I should like to emphasise the necessity for having only men with real human sympathy on the executive staff. I cannot see that mere size has anything really essential to do with the matter.

The more we think, the more we are driven back to the fundamental question whether it is or is not true that an industrial undertaking like a colliery is only an economic machine of which the employed are unit parts. If it is only a machine, then it has no soul to hurt, though it has a body to kick ; and the capital represented by it stands for no spiritual value to be respected, even though it be part of the nation's capital. But we are constantly being told about economic machinery, and about laws of economics which, like the laws of mechanics, have no regard for sentiment, and from which there is no escape. Men very commonly accept in practice the metaphor of the machine, taking this metaphor for a complete representation of industrial reality ; and it seems to me that wholly unnatural instability in the relations between employers and employed is the result. I am convinced that the real driving force behind what is called labour unrest is just human rebellion against what are regarded as inhuman relations.

Had the prevailing sentiment and practice of the members of this Institution not been altogether inconsistent with acceptance of the metaphor of the machine, you would, I know, never have invited me to be your President. In the strength of this knowledge, I will try to examine the metaphor. It is evidently a part of what is commonly believed to be modern realism. We must all bow before reality : mere sentiment is in the long run only a will-o'-the-wisp. If, as so-called modern realism teaches, our world consists of self-existent material things and separate individuals each actuated by self-interest, then these things and individuals behave in accordance with definite laws which we can discover by comparatively simple investigation. We are free to believe, if we like, that God made the material things, the individuals, and the laws of their behaviour ; but this does not matter at all so far as ordinary practical affairs are concerned.

If we enquire whence the so-called realism came, we find that it very gradually took form in science, philosophy, literature, and theology : only at a later time coming to be applied in connection with the relations between employed and employers. In the gray light of this realism spiritual values seemed to melt away from the visible world, as the fantastic appearances of night melt away at dawn ; but only to leave a drab world of physical and economic reality.

There is no use in denouncing physical science and economics as mere materialism. If we want things done, and if we want to avert troubles and dangers from those we care for, we must act in the light of physical and economic knowledge. The more of this light we can throw on practical affairs, and the farther that light enables us to see into the future, the more effectively can we help our fellow-men. Those responsible for the guidance of coal-mining undertakings have constantly to be saying no, in the light of economic and engineering knowledge, to well-meaning but short-sighted proposals, as well as seeking for what will really promote these undertakings ; and those who cannot say no quite clearly are not suited for the positions they occupy.

It is one thing, however, to make use of physical and economic knowledge, but quite another to regard this knowledge as by itself an adequate basis for practice. Here this Institution would, I feel confident, refuse to acknowledge the drab world of physical and economic realism. The capital of a mining enterprise is its credit ; but that credit depends upon the faithful and loyal service of all those engaged in the enterprise, from the lowest paid to the highest paid. Conversely, it depends on careful and loyal care for the interests in the widest sense of all those engaged. The relation among those connected with the enterprise is one of comradeship, and if this relationship is not realised and acted on, the enterprise is unstable and its credit or capital may disappear. A working coal-mine is no mere outcome of what are called economic and physical conditions : it is the outcome of human comradeship, which uses in its own way, and at its own free will, the tools provided by physical and economic knowledge. It has thus a spiritual value capable of inspiring the highest and most unselfish form of service : its credit in the economic sense is credit in a deeper spiritual sense.

These are mere dogmatic statements. What is the justification for them ? Does not actual experience force us back to the drab world of economics in which spiritual values do not count, to the world of each man or group of men pulling against his neighbours ? What I wish to maintain as representing this Institution is that actual experience as we meet it in British collieries is not the drab experience of abstract economics, and that the psychology which represents each individual as simply striving after his own individual interests is bad psychology so far as it is applied to British pitmen, whatever position they may occupy in the industry.

It is just a fact of experience that we care for one another's interests, and anyone who goes underground in a British pit can verify that fact much more quickly than he usually can on the surface. He meets comradeship there; and comradeship in service is what unites us all and transforms the drab world of economics into a variegated world of spiritual values. In the brighter light of better psychology the drab uniformity disappears.

The job of a pitman, and particularly of a mining engineer, is not a soft job; but it is a man's job, and the job of a whole man, not the mere economic man who is scarcely half a man. Those who seek for soft jobs, or think they can make mining into a soft job, had better take themselves off to Utopia : they are not wanted in British pits, nor are hypochondriacs or neurasthenics. When we realise that we are working for and in comradeship with those we care for, hard work and the facing and conquering of dangers and troubles become an honour and not a mere hardship. We then see that physical and economic realism is not realism at all, but a mere superficial representation of a deeper spiritual reality which is in us and around us all the time. In fighting the difficulties and dangers of mining work ; in fighting for the economic stability of mining undertakings, including the interests of shareholders ; and in fighting for the highest welfare of those employed and their families, a mining engineer finds that spiritual reality in his comradeship with those around him. But it is only in the fight that he and the other pitmen who work with him can find it. If mining ever became a soft job, I think that all true British pitmen would with one accord take to some other more worthy occupation.

In this connection there comes into my mind a very earnest and truly eloquent speech, made at the time of the great coal-strike by your then President at a dinner of our sister Institution. He expressed his conviction that the only real remedy for labour troubles lay in a more adequate knowledge of one another and with it a quickened sense of religion. It was assuredly not mere theology that Colonel Blackett had in mind, but practical religion—conduct based on a conviction of the reality of spiritual values and of their dominating influence in all human affairs. What is it that has been undermining that old conviction ? It is the idea that the ultimate reality of Nature is expressed in the conceptions of physical science, and that the reality of industrial undertakings is expressed in the conceptions of economic science. There is thus no room left for spiritual reality in ordinary affairs.

My own work in pure science can be summed up in the conclusion that the mechanical conceptions of physical science break down irretrievably when we endeavour to apply them to life and conscious behaviour, both of which are just a part of what we call Nature. We cannot in the long run dispense with the spiritual conception of Nature ; and I have just tried to point out that the mere economic conception of industrial life breaks down equally hopelessly when we try to apply it to such an industrial undertaking as a British coal-mine. The mere physical and economic conception of reality seems to leave us with a conscious life made up of grim drab experience, variegated by passing sensations and thrills such as those of inferior cinemas, sensational literature and newspapers, and windy oratory, forgotten next day. Such a conscious life is nothing but that of a degenerate. The more earnest-minded men who accept the supposed realism, but rightly despise the world it represents, are, it seems to me, the real moving spirits in labour unrest ; and they are striving after what seem to us to be Utopias. Where they really fail, however, is in not seeing to what an extent there is already a spiritual world around them, realised in the comradeship of daily life.

It appears to me that though we may differ from these men as regards the means, we are on common ground with them as regards the real ends in view, and that there is no reason why we should not work alongside of them over many matters that both we and they have at heart. As regards workmen's organisations, I think we should all go much farther than this : for through their agency much has been done for the good of the mining industry, and the country as a whole, which never could have been done without them. It is impossible to give effective help to people who do not help themselves ; but apart from this, it is both the right and the duty of all connected with the mining industry to contribute such constructive ideas and actions as they can. When these ideas and actions are contributed in the spirit of comradeship we can receive them in the same spirit ; but when they are not contributed in that spirit, then we must just fight them as we fight dangerous gases, coal-dust, gob-fires, falls of roof, water, failing markets, and all the other troubles and dangers of mining work.

If at any time we feel discouraged, we should remember that behind our comradeship there stands the wider comradeship of which the British flag is for us the symbol—a symbol alike of righteous and humane dealing, and of the fearless power that lies behind it. Let us never allow the fickle waves of passing public sentiment to obscure our vision of that wider comradeship.

I think I have now said enough to make my main point clear. It is that whatever may be the immediately apparent values for which this Institution stands, they are, in reality, spiritual values. The spiritual values include, and at the same time transform, the apparent values.

It is not my business to preach a sermon : I am only trying to help you to understand our position. What I have said is based on long observation of the Institution and its members. My memories of it go back to many of those who are no longer with us, and in writing this Address I have had them ever in my mind.

They brought with them to our meetings the comradeship of British pitmen. It seemed to shine in their faces and sound in their voices, and be carried in the shake of their hands. We can read the *Transactions* at home ; but something more subtle than print can convey is conveyed to us at our meetings and dinners.

This Institution has grown from the comradeship of British mining engineers as British pitmen : it stands for that comradeship ; and I am convinced that, so long as it exists, it will continue so to stand.

VIII

REALITY AS SPIRITUAL [1]

WE have become accustomed, in modern times, to regard what we see around us as self-existent material bodies in the activity of which another self-existent thing, energy, is transferred from body to body. Of the practical utility, for many purposes, of this mode of regarding what we perceive there can be no doubt. But when, as we seem bound to do, we extend this physico-chemical realism so as to embrace human behaviour, it becomes what we call materialism, in the cold gray light of which our efforts are benumbed and confused, since we have lost the guidance, such as it was, which religion had seemed to give us.

The scientific evidence in favour of materialism appears on the surface to be strong; and something within us tells us that we must face and embrace truth, whether we like it or not.

[1] " Luncheon Talk " at St. Martin's Church, Trafalgar Square, May, 1932.

It is not, however, as a supporter of materialism, but as one who sees the universe in a very different light, that I am speaking. I am clear, moreover, that there can be no half-way compromise as to the interpretation of our universe. Such a compromise is the theological conception that God created a physical universe, with ourselves in it, and that it was so created that it behaves in the manner described by the physical sciences. To me this compromise stands for materialism in substance, though not perhaps in name : for if we assume that the world around us is simply a physical world, we can then show from observation and experiment that we are part of it.

I wish to go straight to the point. This point is that the universe of our experience is our universe as experienced, and that we do not actually experience it as a mere physical universe, but as a universe which embodies values, with desires, duties, and acts corresponding to them and meaningless apart from them. The universe as merely interpreted physically is artificially stripped of its values, and therefore only an idealised universe. When we regard it fully as the universe of our experience, which it is, we can no longer apply this artificial interpretation, though we still find that for certain limited practical purposes it is both useful and necessary to do so.

This is the main criticism of physico-chemical realism with its materialistic corollary ; and it is a deadly criticism, since it is based on the nature of our experience itself. We have no right whatever to assume the ultimate existence of a universe different from that which we have experience of. The physically interpreted universe is only real as a partial or incomplete interpretation of our experience. This incompleteness is now evident enough to physicists themselves, even in connection with what we artificially distinguish as inorganic phenomena. In connection with what we similarly distinguish as the phenomena of life the incompleteness is far more evident, and, as myself a biologist, I am unable to regard as anything else than a hopeless scientific failure the theory that life can be regarded as simply a physico-chemical process. It is, however, when we come to consider directly the nature of conscious experience itself that the incompleteness becomes most evident.

During the last three centuries it has come to be taken as common sense that what we see and feel around is something entirely outside us, the nature of which is revealed by physical science, and that what is revealed to us in perception is simply this external world, truth being the correspondence between it and our interpretation of it. Now when we interpret physically what we perceive, we interpret it as consisting of separate bodies and their separate relative motions and actions on one another. But this mode of interpretation artificially excludes every aspect of our experience that cannot be interpreted in this way ; and if we make physical interpretation into a common-sense view of what we perceive, we exclude these other aspects. When we perceive the things around us we are perceiving them in much more than their physical and chemical aspects. Let us take as an example what we perceive in reading a book. From the standpoint of physical science the book consists of thin sheets of felted fibres with numerous separate carbon stains upon them. Except that they mostly stand for vocal sounds the individual marks mean nothing to us. But in their relation of succession to one another and their further relation as a whole to the rest of our experience they represent a great deal more. They enter into our interest—into the manner in which we not only perceive other things, but in which we act. Otherwise expressed they enter into the values we set on what we perceive in the present, anticipate in the future, and look back to in the past, and thus enter into our corresponding actions.

From this example we can see that though we can distinguish bodies and their motions in our experience, they possess, in their relations to one another and to the rest of our experience, a reality which physical interpretation does not express, and which it cannot express because it does not do more than set out to represent our experience as that of separable existences and events.

What we perceive is what *we* perceive. By neglecting an essential part of what we perceive we can represent it as a collection of separate sensations or sense-data, with corresponding physical causes. But this ignores the significance involved in each perception ; and indeed, if we probe deeper, as the philosopher Kant did, we find that sensations or perceptions or sense-data in isolation from one another mean just nothing at all. Their relations to one another, to our own activity, and to what appears to us as in the past, or is anticipated in the future, enter into the intimate reality of all the distinguishable elements in our experience.

We find that the details of this experience are, moreover, unified as constituting our interest. What this means is that each distinguishable element in our experience is essentially related to the other elements in such a way that in their relation they constitute values which are actively maintained throughout our experience so as to express what we call our personality. Thus what we experience is not just a collection of separable experiences, separable existences or events, but it is of the very essence of all the elements which we can distinguish in our experience that they are our own experiences, entering into our active personality and not outside of us. How we perceive, as well as how we act, expresses always the unity of personality.

This implies that the universe of our experience is spiritual or personal, and cannot by any possibility be regarded, except for very limited practical purposes, as a mere physical universe. Out of this conclusion, however, arises a further question. Does the universe consist of separate personalities ? If we assumed that it does we should be confronted with facts which are inconsistent with the assumption. When we look into our personalities—into what is involved in our experience—we find that what we acknowledge as truth, right, and beauty are not things which merely accord with our individual interest and thought, or enter into our merely individual personalities. They represent something which appeals, or is capable of appealing, to all men. We find ourselves impelled to cherish and promote them. This is what we are familiar with as moral obligation, and which expresses itself as fellowship or comradeship—for instance, the fellowship of scientific men in the promotion of truth, or just the comradeship of one another in the doing generally of what seems honest and kind.

The fact of moral obligation implies clearly that we are no mere individual personalities among others ; that just as we are not spiritually separated from what we see around us, so we are not spiritually separated from other personalities by any real gulf of being. Hence we are not mere individual personalities which are born and die. But as personality is implied in the very being of our experienced universe, we are compelled, by the fact of moral obligation, to recognise, in what seems at first sight to be our mere individual personality, the presence within us of the all-embracing personality which men call God. In so far as our experience represents what we find ourselves bound to acknowledge as that of God within us, it partakes of objective validity and truth. The world which we see and feel around us and in us, including all its beauty and tragedy, is thus an objective or real world, however imperfectly we may be interpreting it; but at the same time it is a spiritual world, in which God's activity is manifested everywhere and at all times.

Let us look further at this reasoning. It shows us that God is present in us in so far as we seek after truth, goodness, and beauty. But it does not tell us of any world, either now or in the future, which will be free from ignorance, sin, sorrow, and ugliness. It is in the effort to realise moral obligation, and not in the attainment of this effort, that we realise our oneness with God. Our actual attainments, including actual knowledge, are always incomplete. When we consider this further we can see that moral obligation, and indeed spiritual activity of any kind, would have no meaning in a perfect universe if we try to conceive one. It is only in the effort to replace ignorance by relative knowledge, to see and do our duty, to relieve distress, and to avoid and prevent evil and ugliness, that moral obligation realises itself, and that with it God is manifested in us. Similarly, the artist can only produce beauty in presence of muddy paint, refractory marble, or difficulty of expression in language or in terms of mechanical vibration of a musical instrument or human voice; and scientific work is a constant pursuit of knowledge which is never more than partial.

It seems to me that the essential feature of Christianity, and what gives it its real power in a world full of ignorance, sorrow, sin, and ugliness, is the conception of God as not a perfect being dwelling apart from an imperfect world, but as actually present in that world, and entering into the sorrow of its suffering and sin, of which sorrow the Cross is an appropriate symbol. In that wonderfully sympathetic picture of practical Christianity which George Eliot painted in *Adam Bede*, she puts into the

mouth of Dinah Morris the words, " I have seen
with new clearness the meaning of these words,
' If any man love me, let him take up my cross.'
I have heard this enlarged upon as if it meant
the troubles and persecutions we bring on ourselves by confessing Jesus. But surely this is a
narrow thought. The true cross of the Re-
deemer was the sin and sorrow of the world—
that was what lay heavy on His heart—and that
is the cross we shall share with Him, that is the
cup we must drink of with Him, if we would have
any part in that Divine Love which is one with
His sorrow."

These words appear to me to represent, in a
vivid pictorial form, what is specially distinctive
of Christianity, though not absent in other forms
of religion.

It seems to me that religion is obscured by
theology which teaches that God dwells apart,
in perfection and omnipotence. Such theology
leaves unanswered the question why, if so, evil,
suffering, and imperfection are permitted to
exist, and would continue to exist to all eternity
if the old theological conception of heaven and
hell were correct. This teaching is to my mind
neither the Christianity of the Cross nor what is

founded on experience. Ignorant persons may be frightened or coaxed into certain lines of conduct by fear of hell or hope of heaven, but for this they are no better morally, and if nothing but this fear or hope inspired their conduct they would rightly be regarded with contempt.

Religion is based, and, as it seems to me, real Christianity is based, on experience itself. That experience implies that our universe is no mere physical or biological universe, but a spiritual universe of values which can only be expressed as the active manifestation of personality in an indefinite or chaotic background. Our experience implies also that these values are no mere values for individual personality, so that within our apparent individual personalities is the unifying and all-embracing Personality of God. Realisation of this gives us religion. Morality without religion leaves unanswered the question why we are impelled to strive for what is truer, better, and more beautiful. When religion is added, and we realise that God is present to us in our striving, we gain strength, courage, and inward peace, in spite of all our limitations and failures. It is from the inmost reality of our own being and that of our universe of experi-

218

ence that the striving comes, and that inmost reality is the manifestation of God. In so far as we are realising that striving we are immortal and free, but not as mere individuals.

From this account of religion, and of what seems to me the essence of Christianity, it follows at once that Christian religion is a sham unless it is constantly lived in everyday life. There is no weekday world, and no external world, in which religion does not count. The everyday world is the spiritual world ; and if we forget this we are wandering without guidance. It follows also that religion is its own reward. Neither hope of a future heaven, nor fear of a future hell, enters into it. We find the Kingdom of God within us, as Jesus taught ; and it is no limited kingdom, but the universal and eternal Kingdom of God's activity. Religion enables us to face sin, sorrow, and death. We can walk among them with the assurance that God is present amidst them. We can also look back to the remotest past, forward to the remotest future, and outward to the remotest depth of space, with the same assurance : for all of these belong to the universe of our experience.

As you probably know, I am a member of no Church, because there is so much that I cannot accept in the theology associated with existing Churches. It is, therefore, as a free-thinker that I am addressing you, though one whose reasoning has led him to a clear recognition of spiritual reality as the only reality. Do not think that, since I am engaged in scientific work, this recognition alienates me in any way from my work or from my fellowship with other scientific workers. It is just the opposite. We are all engaged in the pursuit of truth, though of different partial aspects of it. The recognition that spiritual reality, as the pursuit of truth, is embodied in all scientific work brings us more closely together ; and we are still together when we are fighting against what seems to us to be bad theology.

Whether my hearers belong to Churches or not, the point which I have tried to make in this short talk is the same. It is that the ordinary world which we see and feel around us is a spiritual world of values, in which we find the manifestation of God. We find it in our comradeship with others in the honest and diligent carrying out of our occupations, in our care for one another, in public services, and in our joint recognition and furtherance of truth and beauty. If we lose sight of this spiritual world we have lost sight of what is alone ultimately real in ourselves, and we are not realising ourselves. Science by itself cannot guide us, since from its very nature it does not deal with the values which are supreme.

Science is not enough. Reason in its highest form as religion, and real religion, extending into every part of our lives, is what, as it seems to me, the world has most need of. Particularly is this so just now, with old theological beliefs, which to a large extent embodied religion, disintegrating in every direction, along with old scientific beliefs, as well as old political beliefs. What I have tried to put before you is an appeal for living and at the same time rational religion.

Not a vitalist - 122